Revision Notes
for
Higher
Physics

Lyn Robinson

Principal Teacher of Physics

Williamwood High School, Clarkston

Editorial assistance by

Andrew McGuigan

Principal Teacher of Physics
St Kentigern's Academy, Bathgate

Published by
Chemcord
Inch Keith
East Kilbride
Glasgow

ISBN   1 870570 72 3

© Robinson , 2000
First reprint 2003

Printed by Bell and Bain, Glasgow

Contents

Unit 1 Mechanics and Properties of Matter

1.1	Vectors	1
1.2	Equations of motion	7
1.3	Newton's Second Law, energy and power	15
1.4	Momentum and impulse	21
1.5	Density and pressure	26
1.6	Gas laws	36

Unit 2 Electricity and Electronics

2.1	Electric fields and resistors in circuits	45
2.2	Alternating current and voltage	57
2.3	Capacitance	59
2.4	Analogue electronics	68

Unit 3 Radiation and Matter

3.1	Waves	80
3.2	Refraction of light	88
3.3	Optoelectronics and semiconductors	94
3.4	Nuclear reactions	112
3.5	Dosimetry and safety	118

Additional Content Statements

4.1	Units, prefixes and scientific notation	124
4.2	Uncertainties	124
	Quantities and units	126
	Formulae	127

Note to students

The course
- This book is designed to cover all of the Content Statements of the revised Higher Physics (Higher Still) Arrangements.

- There are in addition some notes that go beyond the Arrangements but which will be useful to learn. These notes are printed in italic type and marked with a O.

Your revision
- Your revision is most likely to be effective if you stop at the end of each page and try to write out the main points.

- You can indicate your knowledge of each statement with a tick in the ❑ or O at the left hand side.

- Space has been left at the right hand side so that you can make additional notes, or draw attention to questions that you need answered.
  You can also mark statements with a highlighter pen.

- You are more likely to benefit from your revision if you work at a steady rate and follow a study plan.

- A study planner to help you plan your revision is on the next page.

- Calculations should always be set out in full, with all information expressed in symbol form and where necessary changed into SI (basic) units. The standard form of a formula should be written down first and then any necessary manipulation of the formula can be done. Numbers can then be inserted into the formula and the answer calculated.

- Check all your answers for correct units and the number of figures.

- Derivations required are collected together at the end of the book.

- The notes in this book represent a progression from Standard Grade and Intermediate 2 Physics. Your revision should therefore cover all notes from Standard Grade or Intermediate 2 as well as Higher .

- A list of all the relevant formulae for Higher Physics is at the back of the book.

Study Planner

	Tick (√) when revised			
	1	**2**	**3**	**4**
Unit 1 Mechanics and Properties of Matter				
1.1 Vectors				
1.2 Equations of motion				
1.3 Newton's Second Law, energy and power				
1.4 Momentum and impulse				
1.5 Density and pressure				
1.6 Gas laws				
Unit 2 Electricity and Electronics				
2.1 Electric fields and resistors in circuits				
2.2 Alternating current and voltage				
2.3 Capacitance				
2.4 Analogue electronics				
Unit 3 Radiation and Matter				
3.1 Waves				
3.2 Refraction of light				
3.3 Optoelectronics and semiconductors				
3.4 Nuclear reactions				
3.5 Dosimetry and safety				
Additional Content Statements				
4.1 Units, prefixes and scientific notation				
4.2 Uncertainties				
Quantities and units				
Formulae				

UNIT 1 MECHANICS AND PROPERTIES OF MATTER

1.1   Vectors

❑   A **scalar quantity** has a magnitude (size) only.
    A **vector quantity** has both magnitude and direction.

❑   When stating a vector quantity both magnitude and
    direction must be given.

❑   Both distance, *d*, and displacement, *s*, are measured
    in metres, but distance is a scalar quantity and
    displacement is a vector quantity,
    i.e. displacement can be described as the distance
    travelled in a particular direction from the starting
    point.

❑   The distance and displacement for the same journey
    can be very different. Consider, for example, a runner
    on a 400 m circular track. At the end of the race he
    has covered a distance of 400 m but as he has arrived
    back at his starting point his final displacement is
    zero.

❑   Both speed and velocity have the symbol *v* and are
    measured in metres per second, m s^{-1}.

❑   Speed is a scalar quantity and has magnitude only and
    can be described as the distance covered in unit time.

❑   Velocity is a vector quantity and has both magnitude
    and direction. It can be described as the speed in a
    particular direction and is equal to the displacement
    per unit time.

❑
$$\text{speed} = \frac{\text{distance}}{\text{time}} \qquad \text{velocity} = \frac{\text{displacement}}{\text{time}}$$

❑   All variables can be classified as vector or scalar
    quantities:

Scalar	Vector
distance	displacement
speed	velocity
time	acceleration
mass	force
energy	momentum
power	impulse

- Vector quantities have to be added up vectorially, i.e. the directions have to be taken into account.

- The overall effect due to a number of vectors is called the **resultant**, e.g. several displacements in varying directions will give a final resultant displacement from the start.

- The direction of the individual vectors must be taken into account when calculating the resultant by scale diagram (*or by calculation*).

- The resultant of two vectors, A_1 and A_2, can be found by drawing a **vector triangle**. The vectors are added 'nose to tail', i.e. the second vector, A_2, is drawn starting where the first vector, A_1, finishes:

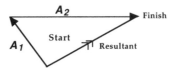

Each vector has to be drawn in the correct direction and to a suitable scale. The resultant is the line joining the first unconnected tail to the last unconnected head. The magnitude of the resultant is found by measuring the length and using the scale in reverse. The direction is given by measuring a suitable angle from the diagram.

- *If the two vectors are at right angles then **Pythagoras' theorem** can be used to calculate the resultant:*

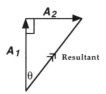

- *The magnitude of the resultant vector is given by:*

$$|\text{Resultant}| = \sqrt{(A_1)^2 + (A_2)^2}$$

- *Direction is given by calculating θ:*

$$\tan \theta = \frac{A_2}{A_1}$$

- Both magnitude and direction **must** be given when quoting a vector answer.

❑ *Example 1*

What is the resultant velocity, relative to the Earth, of a plane which is travelling at 160 m s^{-1} due east, relative to a wind of 40 m s^{-1} from the south-west?

Step 1 Draw a sketch diagram of the situation.

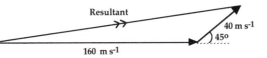

Step 2 Decide from the sketch whether the problem can best be solved by calculation or if a scale diagram is required. If a scale diagram, then choose a suitable scale.

In this case drawing a scale diagram would be easier, since the two vector quantities are not at right angles to each other. A suitable scale might be:

     1 cm represents 20 m s^{-1}

Step 3 Draw the scale diagram for the vector triangle. Angles **must** be measured accurately.

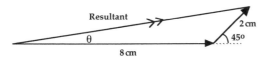

Measuring the length of the resultant gives ~ 9.5 cm. Using the scale in reverse to find the speed gives ~190 m s^{-1}.
Measuring the angle θ gives ~ 9°.
The velocity of the plane is ~ **190 m s^{-1} at 9° north of east** (or at a bearing of 081°).

○ *Example 2*

What is the resultant displacement of an aircraft which flies 120 km north and then 90 km east?

Step 1 *Draw a sketch diagram of the situation.*

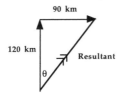

Step 2 *Decide from the sketch whether the problem can best be solved by calculation or if a scale diagram is required.*

In this case, since the two vector quantities are at right angles, the resultant can be found using Pythagoras' theorem:

$$\left| \text{Resultant} \right| = \sqrt{120^2 + 90^2} = \sqrt{22\,500} = 150 \text{ km}$$

Since displacement is a vector quantity the direction must be calculated as well:

$$\tan \theta = \frac{90}{120} \quad => \quad \theta = 36.9^\circ$$

*The resultant displacement is **150 km at 36.9° east of north** (or at a bearing of 036.9°).*

NOTE: *in this case the right angled triangle is an example of a 3, 4, 5 triangle (3 x 30 km, 4 x 3 km, 5 x 30 km); this is often the case and gives a quick way of obtaining the answer.*

NOTE: answers obtained by scale diagrams are normally less accurate than those found by calculation.

❑ Any vector, **A**, can be replaced by two other vectors, acting at the same point, which are at right angles to each other. These two vectors, of magnitudes **A** cos θ and **A** sin θ, are called the **rectangular components** of the original vector:

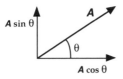

❑ The cos component always touches the given angle.

❑ This can be used to find the effect of a vector in a particular direction, e.g. for a projectile, such as a golf ball, sent off at a velocity **V** at angle θ to the horizontal:

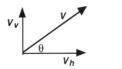

where

$V_v = V \sin \theta$

$V_h = V \cos \theta$

❑ The resultant of a number of forces acting on an object is the single force which will produce the same effect on the object.

❏ Force is a vector quantity and the resultant force due to a number of forces acting on an object can be found:

(i) from a scale diagram, especially if there are more than two forces or the two are not at right angles,

○ (ii) *by calculation, especially if there are two forces at right angles.*

❏ *Example*
Two tugs are pulling a tanker into dock. The angle between the two tow-lines is 80° and each tug exerts a pull of 1×10^6 N. What is the size and direction of the resultant force exerted by the tugs on the tanker?

Step 1 Draw a sketch diagram of the situation.

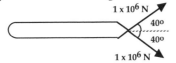

Step 2 Choose a suitable scale for the vector triangle, e.g. 10 cm represents 1×10^6 N. Draw a vector, with an arrow head, to scale, in a suitable direction to represent one force. Then from the head of this vector, draw a second vector in the correct direction to represent the second force. Do not forget to measure the angles accurately.

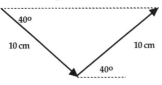

Step 3 Join the first unconnected tail to the last unconnected head.

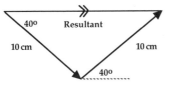

Measuring the length of the resultant gives ~ 15.3 cm. Using the scale in reverse to find the force gives ~1.53×10^6 N

The resultant is ~**1.53×10^6 N**, in a direction midway between the two tugs (at 40° to each tug).

○ *The above example can also be solved by calculation.*

Step 1   *Replace the two vectors by their components.*

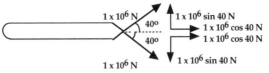
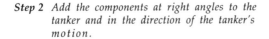

Step 2   *Add the components at right angles to the tanker and in the direction of the tanker's motion.*

At right angles, the sin components cancel as they are in opposite directions.

The cos components add together.

Resultant $= 2 \times (1 \times 10^6 \cos 40)$
$\qquad\qquad = \mathbf{1.53 \times 10^6\ N}$

The direction is midway between the two tugs.

1.2   Equations of motion

❑   **Acceleration** is defined as the change in velocity in unit
     time:

$$a = \frac{v - u}{t}$$

❑   Thus to measure acceleration experimentally, values
     must be found for:

u = initial velocity
v = final velocity
t = the time taken to accelerate from u to v

❑   This can be done using light gates:

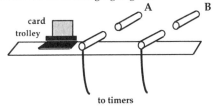

The card is of known length, L , and as it passes through
a light gate it blocks the light, causing the timer
connected to the light gate to start timing. The timer
stops when the card is completely through the light gate.
This happens at both light gates, **A** and **B**.
The timers record:

the time, t_A, taken to pass light gate **A**,
the time, t_B, taken to pass light gate **B**,
the time, t, taken between **A** and **B**.

The initial velocity $u = L / t_A$.
The final velocity $v = L / t_B$.
The acceleration can be calculated from: $a = \frac{v - u}{t}$

❑   It is possible to use a single light gate and timer with a
     double card on the trolley:

Sections **A** and **B** are the same size. As they pass the light
gate, **A** will register a time from which u can be calculated
as above, and **B** a time from which v can be calculated. The
timer also records the time taken, t , between **A** and **B**.
From these values, the acceleration can be calculated
using :

$$a = \frac{v - u}{t}$$

❑ A velocity-time graph can show acceleration, deceleration, and constant speed but it can also indicate the direction of the motion, provided the motion is in a straight line, e.g. for a trolley accelerating along a track, travelling at constant speed, then decelerating to a stop and finally returning along the track:

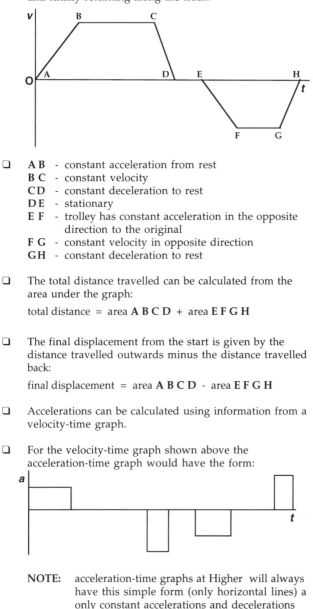

❑ **A B** - constant acceleration from rest
  B C - constant velocity
  C D - constant deceleration to rest
  D E - stationary
  E F - trolley has constant acceleration in the opposite direction to the original
  F G - constant velocity in opposite direction
  G H - constant deceleration to rest

❑ The total distance travelled can be calculated from the area under the graph:

total distance = area **A B C D** + area **E F G H**

❑ The final displacement from the start is given by the distance travelled outwards minus the distance travelled back:

final displacement = area **A B C D** - area **E F G H**

❑ Accelerations can be calculated using information from a velocity-time graph.

❑ For the velocity-time graph shown above the acceleration-time graph would have the form:

NOTE: acceleration-time graphs at Higher will always have this simple form (only horizontal lines) a only constant accelerations and decelerations are considered.

❑ The appropriate values of the constant accelerations and decelerations can be calculated from values given on a velocity-time graph. The gradient (slope) of each section gives the value of the acceleration for that section.

❑ Constant velocity and constant acceleration can be recognised from both acceleration-time and velocity-time graphs. If an object has a constant acceleration, the gradient (slope) of the velocity-time graph will be constant.

○ *If an object has a constant velocity, the gradient of the displacement-time graph will be constant.*

○ *If the information is given in terms of a table of distance (displacement) and time, the distance (displacement) will increase by an equal amount in each time interval, if the velocity is constant.*

> **NOTE:** if the information is given in the form of a table of velocity and time, the velocity will stay the same over successive time intervals if the acceleration is zero; velocity will increase by an equal amount in each time interval if the acceleration is constant.

❑ The **equations of motion** are equations which relate:

s - displacement of object in time t
u - initial velocity of object at time zero
v - final velocity of object after time t
a - acceleration of object
t - time to accelerate from u to v

NOTE:

1. The equations only apply to constant acceleration.

2. The equations only apply to motion in a straight line.

3. The equations are vector equations; apart from time all the quantities are vectors and the direction of the motion must be taken into account.

4. The usual convention is to take the initial direction of the object's motion as positive and relate all other vector quantities to this direction.

❑ Equation 1 comes from the definition of acceleration:

$$a = \frac{v - u}{t}$$

This can be rearranged as:

$$\boxed{v = u + at} \qquad \text{....... equation 1}$$

❑ Equation 2 can be derived by considering the speed-time graph of an object with initial speed u which reaches final speed v after a time t.

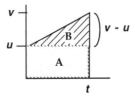

The displacement s is given by the area under the velocity-time graph:

$$s = \text{area A} + \text{area B}$$

$$s = ut + \tfrac{1}{2}(v - u)t$$

But from equation 1: $v = u + at \quad \Rightarrow \quad v - u = at$

Thus:

$$s = ut + \tfrac{1}{2}(at)t$$

$$\boxed{s = ut + \tfrac{1}{2}at^2} \qquad \text{....... equation 2}$$

❑ Equations 1 and 2 can be combined to give a relationship which does not involve time.

Square equation 1:

$$v^2 = (u + at)^2$$
$$= u^2 + 2uat + a^2t^2$$
$$= u^2 + 2a(ut + \tfrac{1}{2}at^2)$$
$$= u^2 + 2as \quad \text{(from equation 2)}$$

$$\boxed{v^2 = u^2 + 2as} \qquad \text{....... equation 3}$$

○ Equations 1 and 2 can also be combined to give a relationship which does not involve acceleration:

$$s = \frac{(u + v)t}{2}$$ .... equation 4

○ Equation 4 means that the displacement is equal to the average velocity multiplied by time.

NOTE: the basic equation $s = vt$ can **only** be used when the velocity is constant; if the object is accelerating the above equations of motion **must** be used.

❑ *Example 1*
A train, initially travelling at 10 m s^{-1} has an acceleration of 2 m s^{-2} for 4 s. What is its final velocity and how far does it travel while accelerating?

Step 1 Put the information into symbol form.

$u = 10 \text{ m s}^{-1}$
$a = 2 \text{ m s}^{-2}$
$t = 4 \text{ s}$

Step 2 Choose the correct equations and complete the calculation.

$v = u + at$ $s = ut + \frac{1}{2}at^2$

$= 10 + (2 \times 4)$ $= (10 \times 4) + (\frac{1}{2} \times 2 \times 4^2)$

$= \textbf{18 m s}^{-1}$ $= 40 + 16 = \textbf{56 m}$

❑ *Example 2*
A car, 220 m away from traffic lights, is initially travelling at 44 m s^{-1} and slows to a halt at the traffic lights. What is the deceleration?

Step 1 Put the information into symbol form.

$s = 220 \text{ m}$
$u = 44 \text{ m s}^{-1}$
$v = 0$ (since the car slows to a halt)

Step 2 Choose the correct equation and complete the calculation.

$$v^2 = u^2 + 2as$$

$\Rightarrow \quad 0 \quad = 44^2 + 2 \times a \times 220$

$\Rightarrow \quad a \quad = \dfrac{-(44)^2}{2 \times 220} \quad = \quad -4.4 \text{ m s}^{-2}$

The acceleration of the car is - 4.4 m s^{-2} or its deceleration is 4.4 m s^{-2}.

❑ *Example 3*

A stone is thrown vertically upwards with an initial velocity of 35 m s^{-1}. What is the velocity after 5 s?

Step 1 Put the information into symbol form.

u = 35 m s^{-1}
a = -9.8 m s^{-2} (gravity; negative since upwards
t = 5 s   is taken as positive)

Step 2 Choose the correct equation and complete the calculation.

$v = u + at$
  = 35 + (-9.8 × 5) = 35 - 49 = **-14 m s^{-1}**

The stone has gone through its maximum height and is coming down at 14 m s^{-1}.

❑ **Projectile motion** occurs when there is a **constant horizontal velocity** and a **constant vertical acceleration** (provided that friction can be ignored).

❑ The vertical acceleration is normally due to gravity.

❑ The horizontal and vertical motions are completely independent. The only factor they have in common is the time of flight.

❑ The path traced out by the projectile is called the **trajectory**:

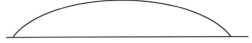

❑ The trajectory for an object with an initial upwards vertical velocity will be symmetrical, provided air resistance can be ignored. Thus the object will return to the ground with the same vertical speed although in the opposite direction, i.e. downwards.

❑ When a package is released from a moving vehicle, e.g. a package dropped from an aeroplane, the initial velocity of the package is the same as that of the vehicle.

❑ The time to the top of the flight can be calculated if the initial vertical velocity is known, since the vertical velocity at the top will be zero and the acceleration is **g** (the acceleration due to gravity).

❑ Since the trajectory is symmetrical, the total time of flight is double that of the time to the top.
This total time of flight applies to both the horizontal and the vertical motion.

❑ If the velocity **V** at an angle θ to the horizontal is given, it must be resolved into components as the horizontal and vertical motions are independent:

$$V_h = V \cos \theta$$
$$V_v = V \sin \theta$$

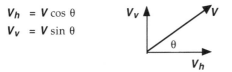

❑ *Example 4*
A ball is kicked horizontally at 5 m s⁻¹ off a 45 m high cliff. Ignoring air resistance find
(a) the time taken for the ball to land,
(b) the distance the ball lands from the foot of the cliff,
(c) the velocity just as the ball lands.

Step 1 Sketch the trajectory and put the information into symbol form.

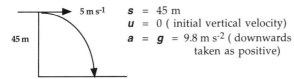

$s = 45$ m
$u = 0$ (initial vertical velocity)
$a = g = 9.8$ m s⁻² (downwards taken as positive)

Step 2 Using the vertical motion to find the time, choose the correct equation and complete the calculation.

$$s = ut + \frac{1}{2}at^2 \implies 45 = 0 \times t + \frac{1}{2} \times 9.8 \times t^2$$

$$\implies t^2 = \frac{45}{4.9} = 9.2 \implies t = 3.0 \text{ s}$$

Step 3 Use the horizontal motion to find the horizontal distance covered in this time.

$s = V_h t$ (use since constant velocity)
$s = 5 \times 3$
$= 15$ m

Step 3 Using the vertical motion to find the vertical velocity at the end of the flight, choose the correct equation and complete the calculation.

$v = u + at$
$= 0 + (9.8 \times 3)$
$= 29.4$ m s⁻¹

Step 4 Combine the final horizontal and vertical
components of the velocity to find the velocity.

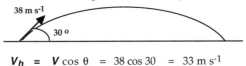

$V_h = 5$ m s^{-1} $\quad |V| = \sqrt{V_h + V_v} = \sqrt{25 + 864}$

$V \qquad\qquad\qquad |V| = 29.8$ m s^{-1}

$V_v = 29.4$ m s^{-1} $\quad \theta = \tan^{-1}\left(\dfrac{29.4}{5}\right) = 80^{\circ}$

NOTE: the angle must be found, since velocity is a
vector and the answer **must** include a direction.

❏ *Example 5*
A golf ball is hit at 38 m s^{-1} at an angle of 30° to the
horizontal. Find
(a) the total time of flight,
(b) the maximum height reached,
(c) the range of the golf ball.

Step 1 Sketch the trajectory and calculate the horizontal
and vertical components of velocity.

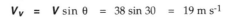

38 m s^{-1}

30 $^{\circ}$

$V_h = V\cos\theta = 38\cos 30 = 33$ m s^{-1}
$V_v = V\sin\theta = 38\sin 30 = 19$ m s^{-1}

Step 2 Consider the vertical motion to find the time of
flight.

$u = 19$ m s^{-1} (upwards taken as positive)
$v = 0$ (at the top of the flight)
$a = g = -9.8$ m s^{-2} (negative since g acts
downwards)

Time to top of flight $= \dfrac{v - u}{a} = \dfrac{0 - 19}{-9.8} = 1.9$ s

Total time of flight $= 2 \times$ time to top $= $ **3.8 s**

Step 3 Use equation of motion to find height.

$v^2 = u^2 + 2as$
$0 = 19^2 - 2 \times 9.8 s$
$19.6 s = 361$
$s = 18.4$ m

Step 4 Consider horizontal motion to find range.

$s = V_h t$ (use since constant velocity)
$s = 33 \times 3.8$
$s = $ **125 m**

1.3   Newton's Second law

❑   **Newton's First Law** states that a body remains at rest or continues at a constant velocity unless acted upon by an external unbalanced force.

❑   **Newton's Second Law** :

$$\boxed{F = m\ a}$$

where F is the unbalanced force in the direction of the motion

❑   Force is measured in newtons, N, where:
"1 N is the resultant (or unbalanced) force which causes a mass of 1 kg to accelerate at 1 m s^{-2}."

❑   Problems involving several forces and objects can be solved by:

(1) In all situations apply:
    Unbalanced force = mass x acceleration

(2) Draw a sketch diagram for the complete system. This must include all masses and any external forces.
    Do not forget forces due to gravity.

(3) If appropriate apply $F = m\ a$ to the whole system.

(4) If only part of the system is to be considered, select the object involved and draw a 'free-body' diagram for that object, i.e. draw a sketch with all the forces exerted on this object, both external and by other parts of the system.

(5) Indicate on the free-body diagram the direction of the acceleration of this object.

(6) Apply $F = m\ a$ to the individual body.

❑   This can be applied to the case of two connected objects.

❑   The tension in a connecting bar or rope is the same at both ends of the rope or bar but in the opposite direction.

❑   *Example*
Find the internal force exerted by a 5 kg block on a 3 kg
block placed touching it, when both are pushed on a
frictionless surface by an external force of 24 N.

Step 1   Draw a sketch diagram.

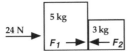

Step 2   Apply Newton's Second Law to the whole
system.

The total mass moving = 8 kg.

The total external unbalanced force = 24 N.

$$F \ = \ ma \ \Rightarrow \ a \ = \ \frac{F}{m} \ = \ \frac{24}{8} \ = \ 3 \ \text{m s}^{-2}$$

Step 3   Consider the single 3 kg block. Sketch a
diagram showing the forces acting on it.

NOTE: The block is part of the system and will
accelerate at the same rate; the only external
force acting on the block is F_1 from the 5 kg
block.

Step 4   Calculate the value of F_1.

$$F_1 \ = \ ma \ = \ 3 \times 3 \ = \ 9 \ \text{N}$$

❑   The same method can be used to calculate the tension in
a rope or bar between two moving objects, e.g. a car
hauling a trailer.

❑ When the vertical forces on an object are being considered, the object's weight must be included.

❑ Sketch diagrams should include the name of the force and its size where this is known.

❑ *Example*
A rocket with a mass of 2×10^5 kg has an initial thrust of 3.8×10^6 N.
(a) Draw a diagram showing all forces on the rocket.
(b) Calculate the initial acceleration of the rocket.

Step 1 Draw a diagram showing all the forces acting. (This should be done even if not asked for in the question).

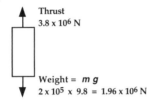

Thrust
3.8×10^6 N

Weight = $m\,g$
$2 \times 10^5 \times 9.8 = 1.96 \times 10^6$ N

Step 2 Calculate the resultant (or unbalanced) force.

$F_{unbalanced}$ = 3.8×10^6 - 1.96×10^6 = 1.84×10^6 N
(direction ↑)

Step 3 Apply Newton's Second Law.

$$F = m\,a \Rightarrow a = \frac{F}{m} = \frac{1.84 \times 10^6}{2 \times 10^5} = 9.2 \text{ m s}^{-2}$$
(direction ↑)

❑ A force can be resolved into its component forces. This can be used to find the effect of the force in a particular direction, e.g. the component of the weight acting down a slope.

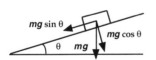

$mg \sin \theta$

$mg \cos \theta$

θ mg

The weight, $m\,g$, can be resolved into two components in terms of the angle of the slope, θ.

Force down the slope = $m\,g \sin\theta$
Force into slope = $m\,g \cos \theta$

❑ *Example*
What is the acceleration of a 7 kg object which is on a slope of 30°, when there is a frictional force of 15 N acting?

Step 1 Draw a diagram showing all the forces acting. Where necessary resolve a force into components.

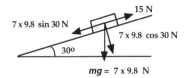

$7 \times 9.8 \sin 30$ N

15 N

$7 \times 9.8 \cos 30$ N

30°

$mg = 7 \times 9.8$ N

Step 2 Consider forces in the direction of motion **only**.

In this case the block will move down the slope.

The resultant force is:

$68.6 \sin 30 - 15 = 34.3 - 15 = 19.3$ N

Step 3 Choose the correct equation and complete the calculation.

$$F = ma \Rightarrow a = \frac{F}{m} = \frac{19.3}{7} = 2.8 \text{ m s}^{-2}$$

❑ Energy is conserved.

❑ If the total energy at any one point is known, then the total energy is known at any other point. This can be used in calculations.

❑ Useful formulae are:

$$E_w = Fd \qquad E_p = mgh \qquad E_k = \tfrac{1}{2}mv^2$$

❑ An apparent energy loss is usually due to work done against friction. This can be used to find the frictional force.

$Fd = \text{lost energy}$ where **F** is the frictional force
d is the displacement

❑ *Example*
A 500 g ball is placed on a slope as shown. It is 3 m high vertically but moves 20 m down the slope. At the bottom it is travelling at 4 m s⁻¹.
Calculate the frictional force on the slope.

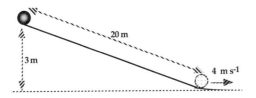

Step 1 Put the information into symbol form and change to basic units.

m = 500 g = 0.5 kg
h = 3 m
v = 4 m s⁻¹
d = 20 m

Step 2 Calculate the potential energy at the start and the kinetic energy at the end.

$$E_p = mgh = 0.5 \times 9.8 \times 3 = 14.7 \text{ J}$$

$$E_k = \tfrac{1}{2}mv^2 = \tfrac{1}{2} \times 0.5 \times 4^2 = 4 \text{ J}$$

Step 3 Calculate the 'lost' energy and thus the frictional force.

lost energy = 14.7 - 4 = 10.7 J

$$Fd = \text{lost energy} \Rightarrow F \times 20 = 10.7$$

$$F = \frac{10.7}{20} = 0.535 \text{ N}$$

❑ Power P is the rate of doing work and is measured in watts or joules per second. If the problem involves **a constant speed** then:

$$P = \frac{E}{t} = \frac{Fd}{t} = Fv$$

❑ In problems involving flow rates assume a time of one second. The power will then be numerically equal to the energy.

❑ *Example*

A 2 kW heater wrapped round a pipe produces a temperature rise of 15 °C in water flowing through the pipe. If the specific heat capacity of water is 4180 J kg^{-1} K^{-1}, calculate the mass flow rate in kg s^{-1}.

Step 1 Put the information into symbol form and change to basic units.

P = 2 kW = 2000 W
c = 4180 J kg^{-1} K^{-1}
ΔT = 15 °C
t = 1 s (assume)

Step 2 Choose the correct equations and complete the calculation.

$E = Pt$ = 2000 x 1 = 2000 J

$E_h = cm\Delta T \Rightarrow m = \dfrac{E_h}{c\,\Delta T} = \dfrac{2000}{4180 \times 15} = 0.032$ kg

This is the mass in 1 s, i.e. flow rate = **0.032 kg s^{-1}**.

1.4   Momentum and impulse

❑   **Momentum** sometimes has the symbol **p**, and is measured in kg m s^{-1}.

❑   Momentum is defined as mass multiplied by velocity:

$$\boxed{\text{momentum} = m\ v}$$

❑   Momentum is a vector quantity and for motion in a straight line one convention is:
an object travelling right $\longrightarrow$ has positive momentum
an object travelling left $\longleftarrow$ has negative momentum

❑   There are two types of interaction between bodies, collisions and explosions.

❑   Momentum is conserved in both types of interaction, i.e. **total momentum before = total momentum after**

❑   The Principle of Conservation of Linear Momentum states that:
"For any interaction between two objects moving along the same straight line, momentum is conserved, **provided there are no external forces acting on the objects.**"

❑   There are two types of collision - **elastic** and **inelastic**.

❑   In an elastic collision both momentum and kinetic energy are conserved.

❑   In an inelastic collision only momentum is conserved.

   NOTE: total energy is conserved in both types of collision but in an inelastic collision some of the kinetic energy is changed into other forms, e.g. energy of deformation (energy required to change shape).

❑   Most real collisions, on a macroscopic level, are not perfectly elastic, although collisions between molecules are.

❑   In an explosion, momentum is conserved but chemical or potential energy is transformed into kinetic energy.

❏ *Example 1*

What is the final velocity of a 4 kg block, initially moving at 3 m s^{-1}, which is hit from behind, by a 7 kg block moving at 9 m s^{-1}? The 7 kg block is slowed down to 4 ms^{-1} by the collision.

Step 1 Draw a diagram of the before and after situations with all relevant masses and velocities.

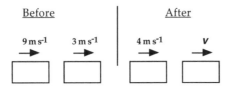

Before   After

9 m s^{-1} 3 m s^{-1} 4 m s^{-1} **v**

NOTE: it is essential to draw this diagram accurately as there are a number of masses and velocities and it is very easy to be confused.

Step 2 Calculate the total momentum before and after.

Before	After
momentum = $m\,v$	momentum = $m\,v$
mom $_{before}$ = $(7 \times 9) + (4 \times 3)$	mom $_{after}$ = $(7 \times 4) + 4v$
= 63 + 12	= 28 + 4**v**
= 75 kg m s^{-1}	

Step 3 Calculate **v** by equating **mom** $_{before}$ and **mom** $_{after}$ since total momentum is conserved during all collisions.

$$75 = 28 + 4v$$
$$47 = 4v$$
$$11.75 \text{ m s}^{-1} = v$$

The 4 kg block moves in its original direction (since **v** is positive), now at **11.75 m s^{-1}**.

❑ *Example 2*
   What is the recoil velocity of a 2 kg gun which fires a
   50 g bullet at 150 m s^{-1}?

   NOTE: when a gun is fired the bullet moves forward
   and this causes the gun to move back because of
   conservation of momentum; the velocity with
   which it moves back is called the recoil velocity.

   Step 1 Draw a diagram of the before and after
   situations with all relevant masses and
   velocities.

   Before   After

   $u = 0$ v 150 m s^{-1}

   | 2.05 kg | | 2 kg | | 0.05 kg |

   Step 2 Calculate the total momentum before and after.

   Before   After

   momentum $= m\,v$ momentum $= m\,v$
   mom $_{before} = 2.05 \times 0$ mom $_{after} = 2v + (0.05 \times 150)$
   $= 0$ $= 2v + 7.5$

   Step 3 Calculate **v** by equating **mom** $_{before}$ and
   mom$_{after}$ since momentum is conserved
   during an explosion.

$$0 = 2v + 7.5$$
$$v = -3.75 \text{ m s}^{-1}$$

   The gun moves in the opposite direction to the bullet,
   since **v** is negative, at **3.75 m s^{-1}**.

❑ **The impulse of a force** is defined as the force multiplied
   by the time for which the force acts:

$$\boxed{\text{impulse } = F\,t}$$

❑ Impulse is measured in N s or kg m s^{-1}.

❑ From Newton's Second Law:

$$F = m\,a$$
$$F = m\left(\frac{v - u}{t}\right)$$

Thus: $\boxed{\text{impulse } = F\,t = m\,v - m\,u}$

❑   Impulse is equal to the change in momentum caused by the force (this equation shows why two different units are used for impulse).

❑   Impulse is given by the area under a force - time graph:

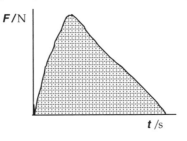

F/N

t/s

❑   In practical situations, the force is not constant but comes to a peak and then decreases.

❑   The area under the force - time graph gives the change in momentum since this is equal to impulse.

❑   *Example*
A golf ball of mass 50 g is hit with a force of 1.6 kN. If the time of contact between the ball and the club is 2 ms, find the final velocity of the ball.

Step 1 Put the information into symbol form and change to basic units.

m = 50 g = 0.05 kg
F = 1.6 kN = 1600 N
t = 2 ms = 0.002 s
u = 0 (not stated explicitly in the question)

Step 2 Choose the correct equation and complete the calculation.

$$\text{impulse} = Ft = mv - mu \quad =>$$

$$v = \frac{Ft}{m} \quad (\text{since } u = 0)$$

$$v = \frac{1600 \times 0.002}{0.05} = 64 \text{ m s}^{-1}$$

NOTE: the force calculated using impulse is the average force acting over the time of contact; the maximum force will be greater than this average value.

❑ When two objects collide, the **total** momentum is conserved. However since each individual object experiences a change in momentum, these changes must be equal but opposite.

❑ Consider two objects **A** and **B** which collide, joining together after the collision. **A** has a mass of 1 kg and an initial velocity of 12 m s^{-1}, while **B** has a mass of 2 kg and is initially at rest.

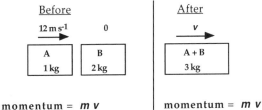

Before	After

momentum = $m\,v$
momentum = $(1 \times 12) + (2 \times 0)$
$\qquad\quad = 12$ kg m s^{-1}

momentum = $m\,v$
momentum = $3v$

Since momentum is conserved in all collisions:

$$12 = 3v$$
$$v = 4 \text{ m s}^{-1}$$

The change in momentum for **A** is $(12 - 4) = 8$ kg m s^{-1}.

The change in momentum for **B** is $(0 - 8) = -8$ kg m s^{-1}.

❑ This can be written:

$$(\Delta m\,v)_A = -(\Delta m\,v)_B$$

Since the change in momentum is equal to the impulse, this can be written as:

$$(F\,t)_A = -(F\,t)_B$$

Also, since the time of contact, t, is the same for both object **A** and object **B**:

$$F_A = -F_B$$

i.e. the forces are equal and opposite.

❑ The Principle of Conservation of Momentum is another way of stating Newton's Third Law:
"Action and reaction are equal and opposite."

1.5   Density and pressure

❑   The **density** of a substance is the mass per unit volume.
Density has the symbol ρ (rho) and is measured in
$kg\ m^{-3}$:

$$\boxed{\rho = \frac{m}{V}}$$ where m is in kg
$\qquad\qquad\qquad V$ is in m^3

NOTE: care must be taken when changing the units of
volume:
$$1\ cm^3\ = 1 \times 10^{-6}\ m^3$$
$$1\ mm^3 = 1 \times 10^{-9}\ m^3$$

❑   *Example*
What is the mass of a cubic centimetre of lead, which
has a density of 11 300 $kg\ m^{-3}$?

Step 1 Put the information into symbol form and
change to basic units.

$$V\ = 1\ cm^3\ = 1 \times 10^{-6}\ m^3$$
$$\rho\ = 11\ 300\ kg\ m^{-3}$$

Step 2 Choose the correct equation and complete the
calculation.

$$m\ =\ \rho\,V$$
$$=\ 11\ 300 \times 1 \times 10^{-6}$$
$$=\ \mathbf{0.0113\ kg}$$

❑   To calculate the density of a substance, the mass and
volume must be measured.

❑   (1) For a **liquid**
The volume can be found using a measuring cylinder.
The mass can be found using the difference between the
mass of the empty cylinder and the mass of the cylinder
with the liquid.

❑   (2) For a **solid**
The mass can be found using a balance. The volume of
a regular shaped object can be found from the
dimensions. The volume of an irregular shaped object
can be found by measuring the volume of water
displaced. This can be done using a displacement or
Eureka can:

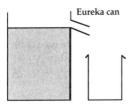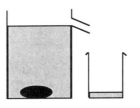

Fill with water to funnel
level

Place object in the water
and collect volume of
water displaced.

The volume of water displaced is equal to the volume
of the object.

❑ (3) For a **gas**
A large rigid plastic container is weighed accurately and
then 'extra' air is pumped into it using a footpump.
The mass of the container and air is measured, the
difference being the mass of the 'extra' air. The air is
then allowed out and collected in a measuring cylinder
by the displacement of water:

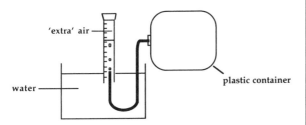

The density of air is given by:

$$\rho = \frac{(\text{mass of container + air}) - (\text{mass of container})}{\text{volume of air}}$$

Care must be taken to ensure the mass is in kg and the
volume is in m³.

❑ (3) For a **gas** (alternative method)
A round bottomed flask with stopper, tubing and clamp, is placed in a plastic beaker for protection and the mass of the whole apparatus is measured, using an electronic balance:

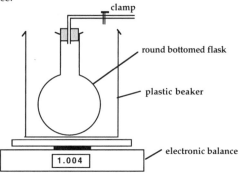

The flask is then evacuated and the new mass measured. The mass of air extracted is the difference between the two readings. The volume of air extracted is found by opening the clamp when the tubing is under water in a measuring cylinder. The volume of air extracted is the same as the volume of water which enters the flask. The density of air is given as before.

❑ The particles in a solid and the particles in a liquid are spaced about the same distance apart.
This means that:

$$\rho \text{ solid} = \rho \text{ liquid} = \frac{m}{V}$$

❑ In the gas, the particles are about 10 times as far apart as those in either a solid or a liquid:

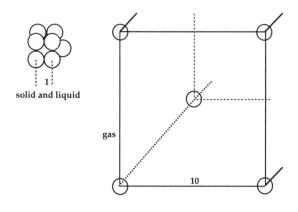

This means that the same mass of gas will have a volume approximately 10 x 10 x 10 = 1000 times that of the solid or liquid.

❏ The density of the gas is

$$\rho_{gas} = \frac{m}{1000\,V}$$

❏ Thus $\rho_{solid} = \rho_{liquid} = {\sim}1000\,\rho_{gas}$

❏ These facts can be summarised for solids, liquids and gases:

	Separation	Volume	Density
solid	1	1	1
liquid	1	1	1
gas	~10	~1000	~1/1000

❏ Given the change in volume when going from the solid, or liquid, to the gas, the particle separation in the gas compared to that in the solid, or liquid, can be found:

$$\frac{\text{particle separation in gas}}{\begin{array}{c}\text{particle separation in solid}\\ \text{or liquid}\end{array}} = \sqrt[3]{\frac{\text{volume of gas}}{\begin{array}{c}\text{volume of solid}\\ \text{or liquid}\end{array}}}$$

❏ *Example*
1 cm^3 of dry ice (solid carbon dioxide) gives 824 cm^3 of gas when it is vaporised at atmospheric pressure. Find the average spacing of the particles in the gas compared to that in the solid.

$$\frac{\text{separation in gas}}{\text{separation in solid}} = \sqrt[3]{\frac{\text{volume of gas}}{\text{volume of solid}}}$$

$$= \sqrt[3]{\frac{824}{1}}$$

$$= \mathbf{9.38}$$

Particle separation in the gas is **9.38** times as great as in the solid.

❑ **Pressure** is defined as the force per unit area:

$$P = \frac{F}{A}$$

where **F** is in N
A is in m²

❑ Pressure is measured in **pascals**, Pa, where 1 Pa = 1 N m⁻²,
i.e. one pascal is one newton per square metre.

NOTE: care must be taken when changing the units of
area:

$$1 \text{ mm}^2 \ = \ 1 \times 10^{-6} \text{ m}^2$$
$$1 \text{ cm}^2 \ = \ 1 \times 10^{-4} \text{ m}^2$$

❑ *Example*
What pressure is exerted by a cube of mass 400 g which
has dimensions of 12 x 12 x 12 cm?

Step 1 Put the information into symbol form and
change to basic units.

$$m \ = \ 400 \text{ g} \ = \ 0.4 \text{ kg}$$
$$A \ = \ 12 \times 12 \text{ cm}^2 \ = \ 144 \text{ cm}^2 \ = \ 144 \times 10^{-4} \text{ m}^2$$

Step 2 Choose the correct equations and complete the
calculation.

The force is the weight of the cube:

$$F \ = \ mg \ = \ 0.4 \times 9.8 \ = \ 3.9 \text{ N}$$

$$P \ = \ \frac{F}{A} \ = \ \frac{3.9}{144 \times 10^{-4}} \ = \ \textbf{271 Pa}$$

❑ The pressure in a liquid varies directly with the depth, **h**,
and the density of the liquid, ρ.

○ *The pressure on a surface is due to the weight of the liquid or gas above the surface:*

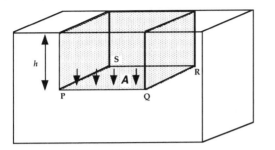

*The surface **PQRS** has a surface area **A**.*

*The volume of liquid above **PQRS** = **A h**.*

*The mass of liquid above **PQRS** = ρV = ρ **A h**.*

*The weight of liquid above **PQRS** = ρ **g A h**.*

*The pressure at the level of **PQRS** :*

$$\frac{\text{weight of liquid}}{\text{surface area}} \ = \ \frac{\rho\, g\, A\, h}{A} \ = \ \rho\, g\, h$$

❏ $\boxed{P = \rho\, g\, h}$ where **P** = pressure in N m⁻² (Pa)

ρ = density in kg m⁻³

g = gravitational field strength (9.8 N kg⁻¹)

h = depth in m

❏ This can be shown experimentally using weighted tubes. In the same liquid, a tube will float at different depths as the weight varies:

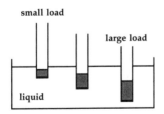

Since the load is supported by the pressure at that particular depth, pressure must increase with depth.

❏ If the load remains the same, the tubes will float at different depths when liquids of varying density are used:

high density

low density

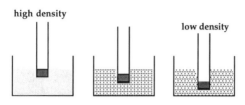

The higher the density of liquid, the smaller the depth required to give sufficient pressure to balance the same load. Thus pressure increases with density.

❏ *Example*
Calculate the pressure due to 10 m of water.
(Take the density of water to be 1000 kg m^{-3}.)

g = 9.8 N kg^{-1} $P = \rho\, g\, h$
ρ = 1000 kg m^3 = 1000 x 9.8 x 10
h = 10 m   = 9.8 x 10^4 Pa

NOTE: this is the normal value of atmospheric pressure; thus a diver 10 m under the water has twice the pressure on him that he would have on the surface., i.e. 1 x 10^5 Pa from the atmosphere and approximately 1 x 10^5 Pa from 10 m of water.

❏ Liquids and gases both flow and they will do so until the pressure is the same at any given level. In mercury barometers, the height of the column of mercury which is supported by atmospheric pressure is measured:

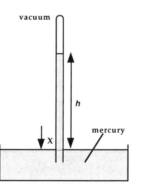

vacuum

h

X   mercury

The pressure on the surface of the mercury, at **X**, is equal to the pressure inside the tube at the same level.

Outside, the pressure is due to the atmosphere:

$P_{outside} = P_{atmospheric}$

Inside, the pressure is due to the column of mercury only, since there is a vacuum at the top:

$P_{inside} = \rho_{mercury}\, g\, h$

Thus: $P_{atmospheric} = \rho_{mercury}\, g\, h$

By measuring h, $P_{atmospheric}$ can be found.

❑   **Manometers** can be used to find gas pressures. A manometer is an open tube containing a liquid.

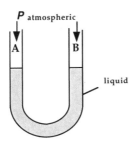

❑   If the end of the tube at side **A** is connected to a gas of unknown pressure, this can become:

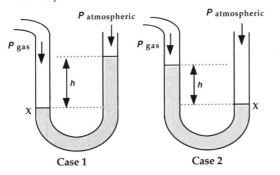

In both cases, the pressure at level **X** is the same on both sides of the manometer, due to the gas or atmospheric pressure, plus on one side, the extra pressure due to the column of liquid of height h.

❑   **Case 1** P_{gas} is greater than $P_{atmospheric}$

$P_{gas} = P_{atmospheric} + \rho_{liquid}\, g\, h$

❑   **Case 2** P_{gas} is less than $P_{atmospheric}$

$P_{gas} + \rho_{liquid}\, g\, h = P_{atmospheric}$

❑   When an object is immersed in a liquid, it experiences an **upthrust**.

❑   When the upthrust is equal to the weight of the object, the object floats.

❑   **Experiment to find the upthrust**
    The weight of an object is found using a spring balance and then the object is lowered into a liquid. The reading on the spring balance is less by the size of the upthrust.

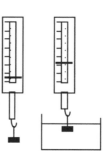

○   *Archimedes' Principle states:*
    "The apparent loss of weight of an object placed in a liquid is equal to the weight of liquid displaced."
    This apparent loss of weight is equal to the **upthrust** *on the object.*

○   *A block of surface area,* **A**, *and vertical height,* **d**, *is placed in a liquid of density,* ρ, *as shown:*

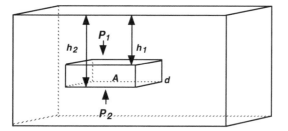

The downwards pressure on the top surface due to the liquid is $P_1 = \rho g h_1$.
The upwards pressure on the bottom surface due to the liquid is $P_2 = \rho g h_2 = \rho g (h_1 + d)$.
The net pressure up $= (P_2 - P_1) = \rho g d$.
The force up, due to the liquid (upthrust) $=$
                                        pressure x area.

upthrust $= \rho g d A$
But: $d A$ $=$ volume of object
              $=$ volume of liquid displaced

upthrust $= \rho \times$ volume of liquid displaced $\times g$

             $= m_{liquid} \, g$

upthrust $=$ weight of liquid displaced

○ *Example*
Will a cube of side 12 cm and mass 1.4 kg float in water of density 1000 kg m^{-3}?

weight of cube in air = $\boldsymbol{m}\,\boldsymbol{g}$ = 1.4×9.8 = $13.7\,\text{N}$

volume of cube = $(0.12 \times 0.12 \times 0.12)$ = $1.73 \times 10^{-3}\,\text{m}^3$

If the cube sinks:
volume of water displaced = volume of object

maximum upthrust = *weight of water displaced by the whole cube*

weight of water displaced = $\boldsymbol{V}\,\rho\,_{\textbf{water}}\,\boldsymbol{g}$
= $1.73 \times 10^{-3} \times 1000 \times 9.8$
= **16.9 N**

Since the maximum upthrust is greater than the weight of the cube, the cube will float. (It will partially sink, until the weight of water displaced is equal to the weight of the cube.)

Flotation or buoyancy
❑ The force $\boldsymbol{F_1}$ on the bottom surface is proportional to the depth $\boldsymbol{d_1}$ of the bottom surface in the liquid. The force $\boldsymbol{F_2}$ on the top surface is proportional to the depth $\boldsymbol{d_2}$ of the top surface in the liquid.
Since $\boldsymbol{d_1}$ is always greater than $\boldsymbol{d_2}$, $\boldsymbol{F_1}$ is always greater than $\boldsymbol{F_2}$. There is always an upthrust or buoyancy force.

❑ Where the upthrust is greater than the weight of the object, the object moves up until the weight balances the upthrust. The object then floats at this level.

❑ Sunken ships can be brought to the surface by filling them with polystyrene balls. These have a very low density, thus a large volume of these balls has a very low mass. They displace the water from inside the ship until the overall weight of the ship is less than the upthrust so the ship starts to rise.

○ *This can also be considered in terms of average density. An object of average density less than that of the liquid it is in will float. Thus a metal ship can float on water, even though the density of the metal is far greater than the density of the water. The metal is only used for the outer casing of the ship, which is filled with air. The overall density of the ship is far less than the metal, and less than the water. Therefore the ship floats.*

1.6   Gas laws

❑   The **kinetic model** of matter explains the behaviour of solids, liquids and gases in terms of the arrangement and movement of the particles which make them.

In simple terms:

❑   (1) In a **solid**
The particles are close together, arranged in neat rows and vibrating slowly, i.e. they move about a fixed position.

❑   (2) In a **liquid**
The particles are still as close together, but have no fixed arrangement and the molecules are free to move anywhere within the bulk of the liquid.

❑   (3) In a **gas**
The particles are much further apart (approximately x10), moving very fast in any direction, through all the space in the container.

In the **kinetic model of a gas**:

❑   (1) A gas is considered to consist of many millions of widely spaced particles all moving at random in all directions and with a range of speeds.

❑   (2) The volume of the gas is the volume of the container holding the particles. The total volume of all the particles themselves is negligible.

❑   (3) These particles do not have any effect on each other except when they collide. All collisions are totally elastic.

❑   (4) As the temperature increases, the average kinetic energy of the particles increases and they move faster.

❑   When the particles of the gas collide with the walls of the container, they exert a force.

❑   The **pressure of the gas** is the sum of all these forces divided by the area.

❑   This force is larger if the particles are moving faster or if there are more particles colliding with the walls.

❑   Thus the higher the temperature and the greater the number of collisions the larger the pressure.

The relationship between the pressure and volume of a fixed mass of gas at constant temperature can be found using the apparatus shown.
The fixed mass of gas is trapped over oil in a tube of constant cross sectional area, so that the length of the column of gas is proportional to the volume of the gas:

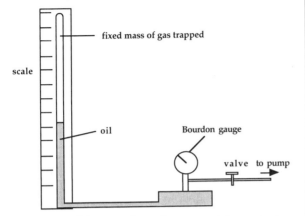

The length of the gas column is measured for various known pressures, varied using the pump. Sufficient time is allowed between readings for the temperature of the gas to go back to room temperature before readings are taken. Graphs are plotted:

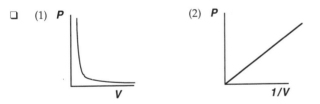

□   (1) **P**   (2) **P**

                    V   **1/V**

□   From Graph (2) the pressure can be seen to be directly proportional to **1/V**, since this gives a straight line through the origin. This relationship is known as Boyle's Law and is usually written:

$$PV = \text{constant}$$ **Boyle's Law**

NOTE: the units of pressure and volume can vary as long as they are consistent throughout the calculation, e.g. pressure can be in pascals, atmospheres, $N\ m^{-2}$ or cm of mercury and volume can be in litres, m^3, cm^3 or mm^3; there is no need to change to basic units in these problems.

❏ Boyle's Law is usually stated as:
"The pressure of a fixed mass of gas varies inversely with the volume, provided the temperature remains constant."

❏ *Example*
A 3 litre cylinder contains gas at a pressure of 40 atmospheres. What volume of gas will be available for use at normal atmospheric pressure?

Step 1 Put the information into symbol form using P_1 for the initial pressure and P_2 for the final pressure, etc.

P_1 = 40 atmospheres
V_1 = 3 litres
P_2 = 1 atmosphere

Step 2 Choose the correct equation and complete the calculation.

Boyle's Law is usually used in the form:

$$P_1 V_1 = P_2 V_2 \quad => \quad V_2 = \frac{P_1 V_1}{P_2}$$

$$= \frac{40 \times 3}{1}$$

$$= 120$$

The total available gas is 120 - 3 = **117 litres**.

NOTE: although the total volume of gas at 1 atmosphere is 120 litres, the gas available for use is less than this, as a volume equal to the size of the container will remain within the container; once the pressure inside and outside the container is the same, no more gas will escape.

❏ The relationship between the pressure and temperature of a fixed mass of gas at constant volume can be found using the apparatus below:

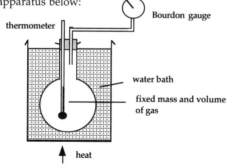

thermometer

Bourdon gauge

water bath

fixed mass and volume of gas

↑ heat

The gas is heated slowly using the water bath so that the whole volume has a chance to reach the same temperature. The pressure and temperature are taken every 10 °C.

❑ A graph is plotted of pressure against temperature:

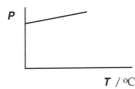

P

T / °C

❑ The pressure increases with temperature but is **not** directly proportional to temperature.

❑ The temperature at which the pressure is zero is found by projecting the line of the graph back until it reaches the temperature axis. The temperature at which this occurs is found to be -273 °C, for any sample of gas, whatever its mass or volume or chemical constituents:

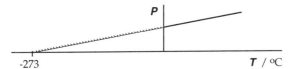

P

-273

T / °C

❑ This temperature **-273 °C** is called **absolute zero**. The **kelvin scale** of temperature starts at absolute zero.

❑ If the graph is replotted with the temperature in kelvin then it becomes:

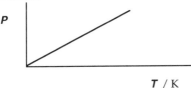

P

T / K

❑ Thus the pressure is directly proportional to the temperature in kelvin, as this is a straight line through the origin:

$$P \propto T$$

$$\frac{P}{T} = \text{constant}$$ where T is in **kelvin**

NOTE: the units of pressure can vary as long as they are constant throughout the calculation, e.g. pressure can be in pascals, atmospheres, N m^{-2} or cm of mercury.

❏ The size of the degree celsius and the kelvin is exactly the same. This means that a temperature change of 100 °C will be equal to a temperature change of 100 K:

degrees celsius

-273	-173	-73	27	127

0	100	200	300	400

kelvin

❏ To change from degrees celsius to kelvin add 273;
to change from kelvin to degrees celsius subtract 273.

❏ Negative kelvin temperatures do not exist.

❏ *Example*
If the pressure of a trapped mass of gas is 1.12×10^5 Pa at 27 °C, what will the pressure of the gas be at 54 °C, assuming the volume stays constant?

Step 1 Put the information into symbol form.

$P_1 = 1.12 \times 10^5$ Pa

$T_1 = 27\ °C = 300$ K

$T_2 = 54\ °C = 327$ K

Step 2 Choose the correct equation and complete the calculation.

$$\frac{P_1}{T_1} = \frac{P_2}{T_2} \;=>\; P_2 = \frac{P_1\,T_2}{T_1} = \frac{1.12 \times 10^5 \times 327}{300}$$

$$= \mathbf{1.22 \times 10^5\ Pa}$$

NOTE: although the temperature in degrees celsius has doubled there is only a small change in the pressure; for the pressure to double, the temperature in **kelvin** has to double.

❑ The relationship between the volume and temperature of a fixed mass of gas at constant pressure can be found using the apparatus below:

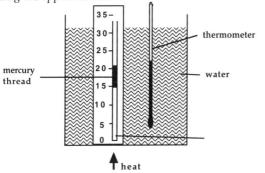

- thermometer
- mercury thread
- water
- heat

The gas is heated slowly using the water bath so that the whole volume has a chance to reach the same temperature. The volume and temperature are taken every 10 °C. The pressure remains constant as the capillary tube is open to the atmosphere.

❑ A graph is plotted of volume against temperature:

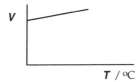

V

T / °C

❑ The volume increases with temperature but is **not** directly proportional to temperature.

❑ The temperature at which the volume is zero is found by projecting the line of the graph back until it reaches the temperature axis. The temperature at which this occurs is found to be -273 °C, for any sample of gas, whatever its mass or chemical constituents:

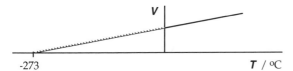

V

-273

T / °C

❑ If the graph is replotted with the temperature in kelvin then it becomes:

V

T / K

❑ Thus the volume is directly proportional to the temperature in kelvin, as this is a straight line through the origin:

$$V \propto T$$

$$\boxed{\dfrac{V}{T} = \text{constant}}$$ where T is in **kelvin**

NOTE: the units of volume can vary as long as they are constant throughout the calculation,
e.g. volume can be in litres, m^3, cm^3, etc.

❑ *Example*

If the volume of a trapped mass of gas is 5 litres at -20 °C, at what temperature in celsius will the volume have doubled, assuming the pressure stays constant?

Step 1 Put the information into symbol form.

$V_1 = 5\,l$
$T_1 = \text{-20 °C} = 253\ K$
$V_2 = 10\,l$

Step 2 Choose the correct equation and complete the calculation.

$$\dfrac{V_1}{T_1} = \dfrac{V_2}{T_2} \;\Rightarrow\; T_2 = \dfrac{V_2\,T_1}{V_1} = \dfrac{10 \times 253}{5}$$

$$= 506\ K$$
$$= 233\ ^{o}C$$

❑ The three gas laws can be combined to give the **General Gas Equation**, involving the pressure, volume and temperature of the gas.

$$\boxed{\dfrac{P\,V}{T} = \text{constant}}$$ where T is in **kelvin**

❑ The general gas equation is usually used in the form:

$$\dfrac{P_1 V_1}{T_1} = \dfrac{P_2 V_2}{T_2}$$

Care must be taken when putting the information into symbol form.

❏   *Example*
The volume of a trapped mass of gas in a gas cylinder is
4.5 litres at -27 ℃, and a pressure of 8 atmospheres.
If the temperature increases to 54 ℃ and the pressure is
reduced to 1 atmosphere, find
(a) the volume which the gas will occupy,
(b) the volume of gas which would be available for use.

Step 1 Put the information into symbol form.

V_1 = 4.5 litres V_2 = ?

T_1 = -27 ℃ = 246 K T_2 = 54 ℃ = 327 K

P_1 = 8 atmospheres P_2 = 1 atmosphere

Step 2 Choose the correct equation and complete the
calculation.

(a) $\dfrac{P_1 V_1}{T_1} = \dfrac{P_2 V_2}{T_2}$ => $V_2 = \dfrac{P_1 V_1 T_2}{P_2 T_1}$

$V_2 = \dfrac{8 \times 4.5 \times 327}{1 \times 246}$ = **47.9 litres**

(b)   The cylinder will retain a volume of gas equal to
the volume of the container.
Therefore the volume of gas available will be:

47.9 - 4.5 = **43.4 litres**

❏   At absolute zero (0 K or -273 ℃), the particles do not
move. It is impossible to actually reach absolute zero, as
even the electrons orbiting the atoms would have to
stop moving and matter, as we know it, would not exist.

❏   At all temperatures above absolute zero, particles are
moving, the kinetic energy increases with the
temperature, and therefore the speed of the particles
increases with temperature.

Explanations of the gas laws in terms of kinetic theory

❑ (1) **Pressure - volume or Boyle's Law** which states:
"The pressure of a fixed mass of gas is inversely proportional to volume at constant temperature."

Since the temperature is constant, the energy and therefore the average speed of the particles is constant. If the volume increases, the particles move further apart. There are fewer collisions with the wlls of the container. The pressure decreases:

$$P = \frac{F}{A} , \quad F\downarrow \quad A\uparrow$$

❑ (2) **Pressure - temperature or Pressure Law** which states:
"The pressure of a fixed mass of gas is directly proportional to temperature at constant volume."

Since the volume is constant, particles have the same distance to go between collisions. If the temperature rises, the particles have more energy and move faster. They hit the walls of the container with greater force and more often. The pressure increases:

$$P = \frac{F}{A} , \quad F\uparrow \quad A \text{ unchanged}$$

❑ (3) **Volume - temperature or Charles' Law** which states:
"The volume of a fixed mass of gas is directly proportional to temperature at constant pressure."

If the temperature increases, the energy and therefore the average speed of the particles increases. The particles hit the walls of the container with a greater force. The volume must increase to give a greater surface area to keep the pressure unchanged:

$$P = \frac{F}{A} , \quad F\uparrow \quad A\uparrow$$

UNIT 2 ELECTRICITY AND ELECTRONICS

2.1   Electric fields and resistors in circuits

❑   The region round an electric charge where it can affect another charge is said to have an **electric field** acting in it.

❑   A charge will experience a force when it is in an electric field.

❑   There are two types of charge, called **positive** and **negative**. (These names are simply labels.)

❑   Like charges repel and unlike charges attract. Thus the direction of the force on the charge will depend on the sign of the charge.

○   *Electric fields can be represented by drawing **field lines**. The field is strongest when the field lines are closest together. The direction of the electric field, by convention, is that in which a free positive charge would move. Electric fields are three dimensional.*

○   ***Radial field** due to a point charge:*

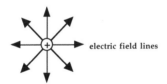

electric field lines

○   ***Uniform field** between two parallel plates (with fringing at the edges):*

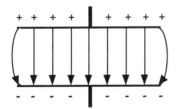

❑   When an electric field is applied to a conductor, the free electric charges in the conductor move.

❑   When charge, **Q**, moves in an electric field, work, **E_w**, is done.

❑ The **potential difference (voltage)**, **V,** between two points is a measure of the work done in moving one coulomb of charge between the two points.

❑ Charge will only move between two points if there is a potential difference.
(Compare this to an object in a gravitational field, which will move if there is a difference in potential energy, i.e. in the heights.)

❑ **The definition of the volt**
If one joule of work is done in moving one coulomb of charge between two points, there is a potential difference of one volt between the two points, i.e. one volt is one joule per coulomb.

❑
$$E_W = Q\,V$$

where E_W is the work done in J
           Q is the energy in C
           V is the potential difference in V

❑ An electron moving parallel to the electric field as shown will be accelerated by the force due to the field. It will gain kinetic energy equal to the work done, i.e.

$$\tfrac{1}{2}\,m\,v^2 = Q\,V$$

-     electron $\bullet\!\!\longrightarrow$ +

❑ *Example*

An electron is accelerated by a 1000 V potential.
What velocity does it acquire?

Step 1 Put the information into symbol form.

$$V = 1000 \text{ V}$$
$$q_e = 1.6 \times 10^{-19} \text{ C} \quad \text{for an electron}$$
$$m_e = 9.1 \times 10^{-31} \text{ kg} \quad \text{for an electron}$$

Step 2 Choose the correct equation and calculate the answer.

$$\tfrac{1}{2} m v^2 = Q V \implies v = \sqrt{\frac{2 Q V}{m}}$$

$$v = \sqrt{\frac{2 \times 1.6 \times 10^{-19} \times 1000}{9.1 \times 10^{-31}}}$$

$$= 1.9 \times 10^7 \text{ m s}^{-1}$$

❑ If the electron is moving initially at right angles to
the field, the force will cause an acceleration parallel
to the field but will not change the motion
perpendicular to the field (forces at right angles to a
motion cannot affect it):

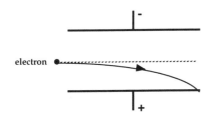

○ *The path of the electron is the same as that of a*
projectile moving under gravity, since it has:

(1) a uniform horizontal velocity (no field),
(2) a uniform vertical acceleration (due to the
   uniform field).

Thus the electron follows a parabolic path.

❑ The **electromotive force (e.m.f.)** of a source is the electrical potential energy supplied to each coulomb of charge which passes through the source. The e.m.f. has the symbol **E**.

❑ Every electrical source can be thought of as a source of pure e.m.f. in series with an internal resistance. A cell should be shown in a circuit diagram as:

❑ The voltage, **V**, measured across the cell is actually measured between **A** and **B**, the two terminals. This is called the **terminal potential difference (t.p.d.)**.

❑ When no current is taken from the source no energy is lost in overcoming the internal resistance and the terminal potential difference (t.p.d.) is equal to the maximum voltage available, i.e. the e.m.f. Thus the open circuit potential difference across the terminals is equal to the e.m.f.

❑ Consider the circuit shown below, with the cell in series with an external resistance **R** (the **load resistor**):

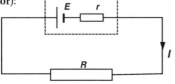

The total resistance of the circuit is **R + r**.

From Ohm's Law:

$$E = I(R + r)$$

$$\boxed{E = IR + Ir}$$

e.m.f = t.p.d. + 'lost volts'

where the 'lost volts' is the voltage used up in overcoming the internal resistance.

❑ The 'lost volts' increase with the current. Thus the larger the current drawn from the source the less voltage is available for the external circuit.

❑   The e.m.f. and internal resistance of a cell can be
    found using the circuit below:

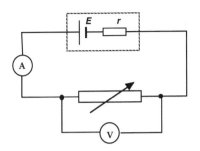

❑   Measure **V** (the t.p.d.) and **I** for various values of the
    variable resistor.
    Plot a graph of voltage against current:

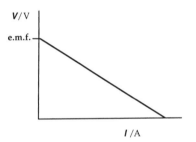

❑   By definition, the e.m.f. is the value of the voltage
    when the current is zero, i.e. the e.m.f. is given by the
    intercept on the voltage axis.

❑   The internal resistance is given by the gradient (slope)
    of the graph (without the negative sign).

❑   The intercept on the current axis gives the 'short
    circuit' current, i.e. the maximum current which
    would be produced if a wire short circuited the
    terminals of the battery.

❏ *Example*

A very high resistance voltmeter connected across a
battery gives a reading of 4.5 V but this drops to 4.2 V
when a 10 Ω resistor is connected across the battery.
Find the e.m.f. and the internal resistance of the
battery.

Step 1 Put the information into symbol form.

$$\text{e.m.f.} = 4.5 \text{ V}$$
$$\text{t.p.d.} = 4.2 \text{ V}$$
$$\boldsymbol{R} = 10 \, \Omega$$

NOTE: by definition the e.m.f. is the potential
difference when no current is drawn;
i.e. the battery is not connected to a circuit.

Step 2 Draw the circuit diagram.

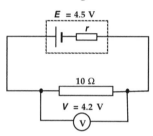

E = 4.5 V

r

10 Ω

V = 4.2 V

NOTE: the voltage across the external resistor is
the same as the terminal potential
difference, as there is only the single resistor
in the circuit.

Step 3 Using the external resistor, find the current
in the circuit.

$$V = I\,R \quad \Rightarrow \quad I = \frac{V}{R} = \frac{4.2}{10} = 0.42 \text{ A}$$

Step 4 Calculate the 'lost volts' and use Ohm's Law
to find the internal resistance.

$$\text{'lost volts'} = I\,r = \text{e.m.f. - t.p.d.} \quad \Rightarrow$$

$$r = \frac{\text{e.m.f. - t.p.d.}}{I} = \frac{4.5 - 4.2}{0.42} = 0.7 \, \Omega$$

- Conservation of energy means that the sum of the e.m.f.'s round a closed circuit is equal to the sum of the potential differences across the components of the circuit.

- **Example**

  Consider a 12 V battery connected to three series resistors, $2\,\Omega$, $4\,\Omega$ and $6\,\Omega$.

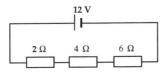

The total resistance in the circuit is $12\,\Omega$.

From Ohm's Law: $\quad I = \dfrac{V}{R} = \dfrac{12}{12} = 1\text{ A}$

Thus one coulomb of charge is passing each point in the circuit every second.

On passing through the battery, the coulomb of charge gains 12 J of energy (definition of the volt).

Passing through the $6\,\Omega$ resistor takes:

$$V = I\,R = 1 \times 6 = 6\text{ V}$$

Thus the coulomb of charge loses:

$$E_w = Q\,V = 1 \times 6 = 6\text{ J}$$

which is transformed into heat.

Similarly the coulomb of charge loses 4 J passing through the $4\,\Omega$ resistor and 2 J through the $2\,\Omega$ resistor.

- After passing through the three resistors, the coulomb of charge has given up all of its energy and has to pass through the battery again to collect more energy.

-
$$\text{e.m.f.} = \text{p.d.}(R_1) + \text{p.d.}(R_2) + \text{p.d.}(R_3)$$

$$\text{e.m.f.} = I\,R_1 + I\,R_2 + I\,R_3$$

- *This is expressed formally as "Kirchoff's Voltage Law".*

❑ The total resistance of resistors in series, R_s, can be deduced from conservation of energy:

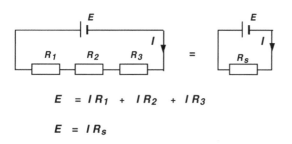

$$E = IR_1 + IR_2 + IR_3$$

$$E = IR_s$$

In a series circuit the current is constant, so:

$$\boxed{R_s = R_1 + R_2 + R_3}$$

❑ The total resistance of resistors in parallel, R_p, can be deduced from conservation of charge (current):

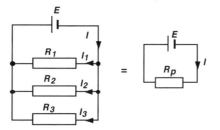

The charge leaving the battery per second (current) is equal to the charge passing through the three resistors per second (current):

$$I = I_1 + I_2 + I_3$$

$$\frac{E}{R_p} = \frac{E}{R_1} + \frac{E}{R_2} + \frac{E}{R_3}$$

The voltage across each resistor is **E**, so:

$$\boxed{\frac{1}{R_p} = \frac{1}{R_1} + \frac{1}{R_2} + \frac{1}{R_3}}$$

- Resistors are used as voltage dividers:

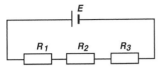

potential difference across $R_1 = \dfrac{R_1}{(R_1 + R_2 + R_3)} \times E$

potential difference across $R_2 = \dfrac{R_2}{(R_1 + R_2 + R_3)} \times E$

potential difference across $R_3 = \dfrac{R_3}{(R_1 + R_2 + R_3)} \times E$

- A **Wheatstone bridge** consists of four resistors as shown:

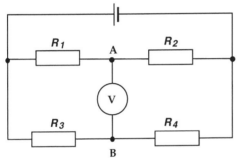

- The voltmeter measures th potential difference between **A** and **B**.

- When the bridge is balanced there is a zero reading on the voltmeter.

- For a balanced Wheatstone Bridge:

$$\frac{R_1}{R_2} = \frac{R_3}{R_4}$$

- This is called a "**null method**" since it relies on the meter reading zero.

- *Sometimes a very sensitive ammeter, called a galvanometer can be used instead of a voltmeter. When the bridge is balanced there is no current through the galvanometer.*

❑ A null method is normally more accurate than methods which involve taking readings as it does not rely on the accuracy of the meters. Even if the meter has been wrongly calibrated it will not affect the answer provided the meter is sensitive, i.e. registers a movement for a very small voltage (*or current*).

❑ In normal use R_1 and R_2 would be resistors of known value, usually with a simple ratio, e.g. 1:10. unknown resistor. The resistance R_3 would be adjusted until the meter reads zero.

R_3 would be a resistance box and R_4 would be the

○ *Since a galvanometer is sensitive, it can be easily damaged and is usually protected by a large value resistor in series. There is a switch in parallel to bypass the resistor when the bridge is close to balance, so that the full sensitivity of the meter can be used:*

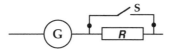

○ *One arm of the Wheatstone bridge, i.e. R_1 and R_2, can be replaced by a length of resistance wire, normally 1 m (100 cm) long. This is called a Metre bridge. Since resistance is proportional to length provided the wire has constant cross-sectional area:*

$$\frac{R_1}{R_2} = \frac{L_1}{L_2}$$

But for a Metre bridge:

$$L_2 = 100 - L_1$$

where the lengths L_1 and L_2 are measured in centimetres

$$\boxed{\frac{L_1}{100 - L_1} = \frac{R_1}{R_2}}$$

❑ The Wheatstone bridge (*and the Metre bridge*) are known as '**Bridge circuits**'.

❑ If a Wheatstone bridge is initially balanced and the value of one of the resistors is changed by a small amount ΔR, the out of balance potential difference across the voltmeter is proportional to ΔR :

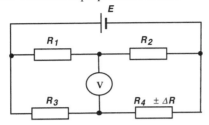

❑ When ΔR is zero, the bridge is balanced and the voltmeter shows a zero reading.

❑ When ΔR is not zero, V is proportional to ΔR :

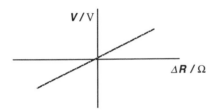

○ *The linear relationship is only true for ΔR up to ~10% of the value of R_4 at balance.*

❑ The resistor R_4 can be an LDR, thermistor, strain gauge or any other component where the resistance varies. The voltmeter can be calibrated to read light intensity, temperature, strain or any other relevant physical quantity directly.

❏ *Example*

The Wheatstone bridge circuit shown is balanced.
What is the value of the unknown resistor R_4 if
$R_1 = 100\ \Omega$, $R_2 = 1000\ \Omega$ and R_3 is a resistance box set
to a resistance of 600 Ω?

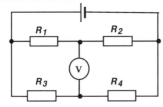

Since the bridge is balanced:

$$\frac{R_1}{R_2} = \frac{R_3}{R_4}$$

$$\Rightarrow\ \ R_4 = \frac{R_2\ R_3}{R_1}$$

$$= \frac{1000\ \times\ 600}{100}$$

$$=\ 6000\ \Omega$$

2.2   Alternating current and voltage

❑   Alternating quantities (current and voltage) can be
studied using an oscilloscope.

❑   Oscilloscopes are calibrated to give:
(1) on the x - axis   -   time per cm (time base)
(2) on the y - axis   -   volts per cm (gain)

❑   An a.c. signal will appear on the oscilloscope screen:

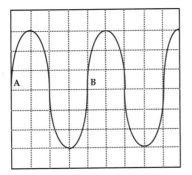

❑   The period of the wave is the time taken for one
wavelength to pass a point and is represented on the
screen by **AB**. This is equivalent to 4 cm in this case.
Thus the period of the wave is 4 x 'time per
centimetre' setting on the time base.

❑   The frequency of the wave can be calculated if the
period is known, since:

$$f \; = \; \frac{1}{T}$$

❑   The amplitude of the wave shown is 3 cm.
Thus the peak voltage is 3 x 'volts per centimetre'
setting on the gain control.

❑   The peak voltage is greater than the root mean square
(r.m.s.) voltage.

❑   The value quoted for a.c. quantities, e.g. 230 V for the
mains, is the r.m.s. value.

❑   The effective or r.m.s. value of an alternating
quantity (current or voltage) is defined as the d.c.
value which causes the same heating effect.

❑ The peak voltage and the r.m.s. voltage are related:

$$V_{peak} = \sqrt{2}\ V_{r.m.s.}$$

❑ Similarly the peak current and the r.m.s. current for a sine wave are related by:

$$I_{peak} = \sqrt{2}\ I_{r.m.s.}$$

❑ Ohm's Law can be applied for an alternating quantity of any waveform:

$$V_{peak} = I_{peak}\ R$$
$$V_{r.m.s.} = I_{r.m.s.}\ R$$

❑ *Example*

What is the peak current for a 100 Ω resistor connected to a mains supply (which is a sine wave)?

Step 1 Put the information into symbol form.

$$R = 100\ \Omega$$
$$V_{r.m.s.} = 230\ V$$

Step 2 Choose the correct equations and calculate the answer.

$$V_{r.m.s.} = I_{r.m.s.}\ R \quad =>$$

$$I_{r.m.s.} = \frac{V_{r.m.s.}}{R} = \frac{230}{100} = 2.3\ A$$

$$I_{peak} = \sqrt{2}\ I_{r.m.s.} = \sqrt{2} \times 2.3 = 3.3\ A$$

❑ In a.c. circuits, components must be able to withstand the peak current and voltage without damage.

❑ The current through a resistor is unaffected by changes of frequency:

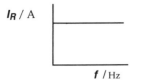

I_R / A

f / Hz

2.3   Capacitance

❑   In its simplest form, a capacitor consists of two metal
    plates with an insulator in between.

❑   The symbol for a capacitor is: ⊣⊢

❑   A capacitor stores charge.

❑   An uncharged capacitor is connected to a battery:

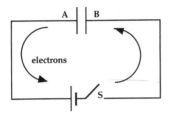

As soon as the switch is closed, electrons move from
the battery to plate **B** of the capacitor.
As electrons are building up on plate **B** they repel
electrons from plate **A** back to the battery.
Although no electrons pass through the insulator
between the plates of the capacitor there is a current in
the external circuit.
As the electrons build up on plate **B**, a potential
difference is produced between plates **A** and **B** which
opposes the supply voltage.
When the potential difference between the plates of
the capacitor is equal to the supply voltage, there is
no more flow of charge.
The capacitor is said to be **fully charged**.

❑   The rate of flow of charge, or the current, is greatest
    when the capacitor is initially uncharged and
    reduces to zero when the capacitor is fully charged.

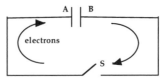

If the battery is disconnected and wires placed across the capacitor as shown, then as soon as the switch **S** is closed, electrons from plate **B** are attracted round the circuit to plate **A**.

There is a current in the external circuit until all the excess electrons have left plate **B**.

The capacitor is said to be **fully discharged.**

❑ The current is greatest when the capacitor is fully charged and reduces to become zero when the capacitor is fully discharged.

Note that this discharging current is in the opposite direction to the original charging current.

❑ The **capacitance, C**, of a capacitor is a measure of its ability to store charge. It is measured in **farads, F.**

❑ The capacitance depends on the physical construction of the capacitor. The farad is a very large unit of capacitance so practical capacitors usually have values measured in microfarads (10^{-6} F), nanofarads (10^{-9} F) or picofarads (10^{-12} F).

○ *An electrophorus consists of an insulating plate and a metal plate on an insulating handle.*

The insulating plate is charged by friction.

If the metal plate is placed on the charged insulating plate and touched by a hand, it will be charged. It will always collect exactly the same amount of charge.

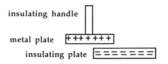

Thus the electrophorus can be used to transport ***equal quantites*** *of charge.*

❑ A coulombmeter is a meter used to measure a quantity of charge, **Q**, in coulombs.

❑ The two metal plates of the capacitor are connected to a coulombmeter. Units of charge are added one at a time using an electrophorus. The potential difference across the plates is measured:

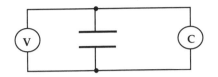

Each time another unit of charge is added, readings are taken on both the voltmeter and coulombmeter.

❑ A graph of potential difference, **V**, against charge, **Q**, would be:

Thus the charge, **Q**, and the potential difference, **V**, are proportional to each other.

❑ The slope of the graph is equal to the capacitance of the capacitor.

❑
$$C = \frac{Q}{V}$$

where **C** is the capacitance in F
Q is the charge in C
V is the potential difference in V

❑ Thus one farad is equal to one coulomb per volt.

❑ *Example*

How much charge will a 10 μF capacitor store when it is connected to a potential difference of 12 V?

Step 1 Put the information into symbol form and change to basic units.

C = 10 μF = 10 x 10^{-6} F
V = 12 V

Step 2 Choose the correct equation and complete the calculation.

$$C = \frac{Q}{V} \quad => \quad Q = CV$$
$$= 10 \times 10^{-6} \times 12$$
$$= 120 \ \mu C$$

❑ Work has to be done to charge a capacitor. The first electron placed on one plate repels the next. The more electrons already in place on the metal plate, the stronger the force of repulsion which has to be overcome to add more charge and so the greater the work that has to be done.

❑ This work is stored as energy in the capacitor. The energy stored in the capacitor is given by the area under the charge/voltage graph. This gives:

$$E = \frac{1}{2} Q V$$

Also, since $Q = CV$ then $E = \frac{1}{2}(CV)V = \frac{1}{2}CV^2$

and since $V = \frac{Q}{C}$ then $E = \frac{1}{2}Q\left(\frac{Q}{C}\right) = \frac{1}{2}\frac{Q^2}{C}$

❑
$$\boxed{E = \frac{1}{2}QV = \frac{1}{2}CV^2 = \frac{1}{2}\frac{Q^2}{C}}$$

where E is the energy in J
Q is the charge in C
V is the potential difference in V
C is the capacitance in F

NOTE: take care not to confuse the formula for the energy stored in a **capacitor** with the formula for energy on page 46.

□ *Example*

How much energy is stored in a 100 μF capacitor when it is charged to 10 V?

Step 1 Put the information into symbol form and change to basic units.

$$C = 100 \, \mu F = 100 \times 10^{-6} \, F = 10^{-4} \, F$$
$$V = 10 \, V$$

Step 2 Choose the correct equation and complete the calculation.

$$E = \frac{1}{2} C V^2 = \frac{1}{2} \times 10^{-4} \times 10^2 = 5 \times 10^{-3} \, J$$

□ **Charge and discharge characteristics of capacitors**

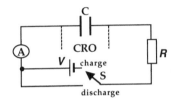

(1) **Charge characteristics**

□ When the switch is moved to the charge position the capacitor charges up.

□ The graphs of potential difference, V, and current, I, against time, t, are:

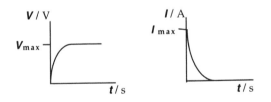

□ The current is zero when the potential difference reaches a maximum.

□ The maximum potential difference across the capacitor, V_{max}, is equal to the supply voltage, V_{supply}.

❑ The maximum current is determined by the size of the resistance, since at the moment the switch is closed all the supply voltage is across the resistor:

$$I_{max} = \frac{V_{supply}}{R}$$

NOTE : when drawing graphs, numerical values for V_{max} and I_{max} should be included if there is enough information in the question to calculate them, even if they are not explicitly asked for.

(2) **Discharge characteristics**

❑ When the switch in the previous circuit is moved to the discharge position, the capacitor discharges:

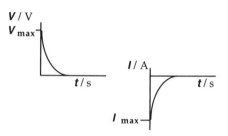

❑ The values of V_{max} and I_{max} are the same as in charging but the direction of the current is reversed.

NOTE: this is only true provided the resistance in the external circuit remains constant; if the battery is replaced by a wire, the resistance is only constant if the internal resistance of the battery is negligible.

❑ If the value of the resistor or of the capacitor is increased, it takes longer for the capacitor to become fully charged or discharged.

❑ *Example*
   (a) What is the maximum voltage across the capacitor and the maximum current in the circuit shown?
   (b) How much energy is stored by the fully charged capacitor?

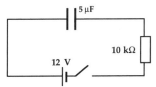

Step 1 Put the information into symbol form and change to basic units.

$$R = 10\,k\Omega = 10\,000\,\Omega$$
$$C = 5\,\mu F = 5\times10^{-6}\,F$$
$$V = 12\,V \text{ (maximum voltage is equal to supply)}$$

Step 2 Choose correct equations and complete the calculation.

(a) $I_{max} = \dfrac{V}{R} = \dfrac{12}{10\,000} = 1.2\times10^{-3}\,A = 1.2\,mA$

(b) $E = \dfrac{1}{2}CV^2 = \dfrac{5\times10^{-6}\times(12)^2}{2} = 3.6\times10^{-4}\,J$

❑ **Capacitors in a.c.**

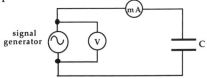

The voltmeter has to be an a.c. type and is used to check that the voltage of the signal generator remains constant. The frequency of the signal generator is varied and the current measured.

❑ A graph of current against frequency gives:

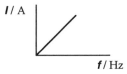

❑ The current through a capacitor in an a.c. circuit is directly proportional to the frequency of the supply.

Uses of capacitors

❏   Capacitors block d.c. but allow a.c. to pass.

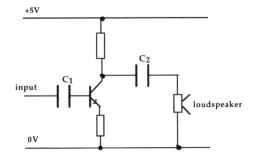

This is part of the circuit of an amplifier. Capacitor
C_2 blocks the d.c. and only allows a.c. through the
speaker. The d.c. is necessary to bias the transistor,
but it could damage the coils of the loudspeaker.

❏   Capacitors are also used to direct high and low
    frequencies to the appropriate speakers in a hi-fi
    system.

❏   Along with other circuit elements, capacitors are
    used to tune radio circuits.

❏   Capacitors store charge and this can be used to
    smooth the output of a rectified power supply.
    Rectification means changing a.c. to d.c.

❏   The simplest way of achieving this is to use a diode
    in series with the supply, since diodes only allow
    current in one direction. This is called half-wave
    rectification, since only half of the input, usually a
    sine wave, is allowed through the circuit.

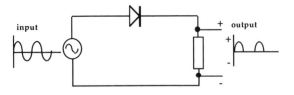

The output voltage is always of the same polarity
but it falls to zero every half cycle, which may not be
desirable with many circuit components.

❑ If a capacitor is placed in parallel with the output resistor, it can store charge while the diode is conducting and release that charge when the diode is blocking the supply or not conducting. Therefore the voltage through the resistor does not fall to zero. The output is said to be **smoothed**.

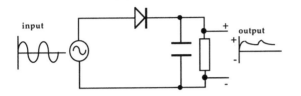

In practice, four diodes are sometimes used to give full wave rectification. Then a smoothing capacitor is included to give a stable smooth d.c. output.

2.4   Analogue electronics

❑   An analogue signal is constantly variable, while a
    digital signal can only have particular values, often
    only two states, i.e. on and off.

❑   **An operational amplifier (op-amp)** has two inputs and
    one output. The inputs are called the inverting and
    non-inverting inputs.

❑   The symbol for an op-amp is:

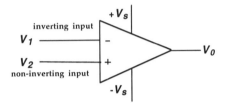

    The supply voltage is often omitted in circuit diagrams.

❑   An ideal op-amp has:
    (1) zero input current because it has infinite input
        resistance,
    (2) no potential difference between the inverting and
        non-inverting inputs.

❑   When a signal V_1 is applied to the negative or
    inverting input of an op-amp an amplified output
    which is out of phase with the input by 180° is obtained.

❑   When a signal V_2 is applied to the positive or non-
    inverting input of an op-amp an amplified output
    which is in phase with the input is obtained.

	Inverting input	Non-inverting input
❑ Input	⌒⌄	⌒⌄
❑ Output	⌄⌒	⌒⌄

❑ A signal V_{in} can be applied to the inverting input of an op-amp as shown:

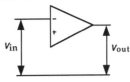

The op-amp is being used in the **inverting mode** and its gain is given by:

$$\frac{V_{out}}{V_{in}}$$

❑ When two signals are applied together at the two inputs, the op-amp amplifies the difference between the two input signals. The effective input signal to the amplifier is then $(V_2 - V_1)$.

○ *An op-amp typically has a gain of about 100 000.*

○ *This gain is limited to a fairly narrow range of frequencies. At higher frequencies the gain falls:*

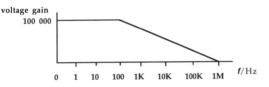

❑ An op-amp is sometimes used with **negative feedback**, i.e. some of the output signal is returned to the inverting input:

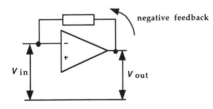

○ *If **negative feedback** is used, the voltage gain is reduced but remains constant over a larger range of frequencies:*

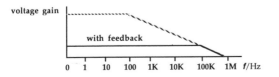

❑ In **inverting mode**, the non-inverting input is connected directly to earth.

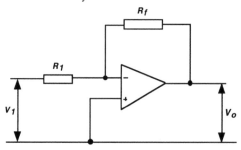

❑ In **inverting mode**, the gain is given by:

$$\frac{V_o}{V_1} = \frac{-R_f}{R_1}$$

❑ Thus the overall gain of the amplifier with feedback depends only on the size of the input resistor and the size of the feedback resistor.

❑ *Example*
   (a) How is the op-amp being used in the circuit shown?
   (b) What is the output voltage, V_o?

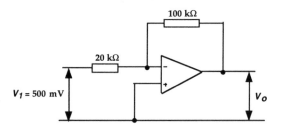

   (a) The op-amp is being used in inverting mode.
   (There are no resistors connected to the positive input and the signal is applied to the inverting input.)

(b)

Step 1 Put the information into symbol form and change to basic units.

$$V_1 = 500\,\text{mV} = 0.5\,\text{V}$$
$$R_f = 100\,\text{k}\Omega \qquad \text{(leave in k}\Omega\text{ as the ratio of}$$
$$R_1 = 20\,\text{k}\Omega \qquad \qquad \text{the resistors is used)}$$

Step 2 Choose the correct equation and calculate the answer.

$$\frac{V_1}{R_1} = \frac{-V_o}{R_f} \qquad \Rightarrow \qquad V_o = \frac{-R_f\ V_1}{R_1}$$

$$= -\frac{100}{20} \times 0.5$$

$$= -2.5\,\text{V}$$

○ *Since the input resistance of an op-amp is so high, two signals can be applied to the inverting input without affecting each other. In this way, the op-amp can be used to add or subtract signals.*

○

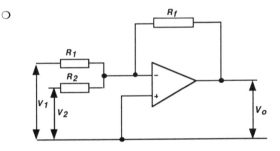

In this case:

$$V_o = V_1 \left(\frac{-R_f}{R_1}\right) + V_2 \left(\frac{-R_f}{R_1}\right)$$

If $R_1 = R_2 = R_f$, then:

$$V_o = -(V_1 + V_2)$$

*i.e. the output is the sum of the inputs in size. This is called a **summing amplifier**.*

○ *If one of the inputs, V_1, is made negative then the circuit can perform subtraction,*

i.e. $\qquad V_o = V_1 - V_2$

○ A digital signal, often a binary number, can be converted to an analogue signal, by choosing suitable values for input and feedback resistors in a summing amplifier:

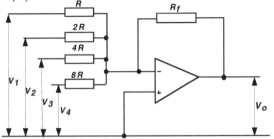

With the circuit shown the output is given by:

$$V_o = -\left\{V_1\left(\frac{R_f}{R}\right) + V_2\left(\frac{R_f}{2R}\right) + V_3\left(\frac{R_f}{4R}\right) + V_4\left(\frac{R_f}{8R}\right)\right\}$$

and if $R_f = R$, this reduces to:

$$V_o = -\left(V_1 + \frac{V_2}{2} + \frac{V_3}{4} + \frac{V_4}{8}\right)$$

○ If the inputs V_1 to V_4 are supplied by a binary counter, they can each be only high or low, for simplicity 8 V or 0 V. For example, if the binary counter is displaying 1100 binary (12 decimal), then the inputs would be:

$$V_1 = 8\,V$$
$$V_2 = 8\,V$$
$$V_3 = 0\,V$$
$$V_4 = 0\,V$$

and the output would be:

$$V_o = -\left(8 + \frac{8}{2} + \frac{0}{4} + \frac{0}{8}\right)$$
$$= -12\,V$$

Thus this circuit performs the function of digital to analogue conversion (DAC).

❑ The output voltage of an op-amp cannot exceed the supply voltage, either positive or negative.
In practice the output voltage is only about 85 % of the supply. Thus using a ± 15 V supply, the maximum output voltage is ± 13.5 V. When the output voltage reaches its maxiumum value the op-amp is said to be **saturated**.

NOTE: it is incorrect to say that the output voltage saturates; it is the op-amp which saturates.

❑ An amplifier can be driven into saturation either by increasing the gain for a given input signal or by increasing the size of the input signal.

❑ Consider the circuit below:

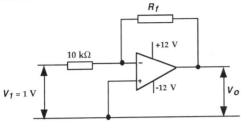

If R_f can have values of 50 kΩ, 100 kΩ, 150 kΩ and 200 kΩ, then the amplifier gain is variable in steps.

The output is given by: $\quad V_o \; = \; \dfrac{-R_f \times 1}{10\,000}$

R_f	Gain	V_o
50 kΩ	-5	-5 V
100 kΩ	-10	-10 V
150 kΩ	-15	-12 V
200 kΩ	-20	-12 V

For the last two entries in the table, the amplifier is driven into saturation and the output is therefore equal to the supply voltage. (In practice a value about 85% of the supply voltage will be reached.)

❏

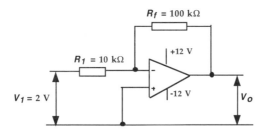

In the circuit shown, the gain is:

$$\frac{-R_f}{R_1} = \frac{-100}{10} = -10$$

This would be expected to give an output voltage of:

$$V_o = -10 \times 2 = -20\ \mathbf{V}$$

However this is greater than the supply voltage (-12 V) so the amplifier is being driven into saturation and the output voltage is about 85% of -12 V, i.e. -10.2 V. This is called the **saturation voltage**.

❏ While saturation is sometimes a problem, for example, causing distortion of an audio input signal, it can also be an advantage, e.g. in producing square waves from sine waves:

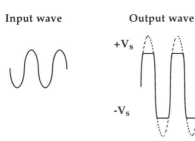

The amplified sine wave would be the output if the supply was high enough but the wave reaches saturation and so a square wave is output, by over amplifying the input sine wave.

Differential mode

❑ When an op-amp is connected as shown below, it is said to be operating in **differential mode**, or as a differential amplifier:

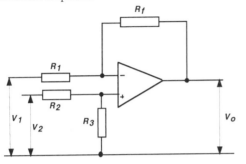

○ *The resistor R_3 is usually chosen so that:*

$$\frac{R_3}{R_2} = \frac{R_f}{R_1}$$

The gain is the same for both input voltages.

❑ In differential mode, the op-amp amplifies the **difference** between the two input voltages, V_1 and V_2.

❑ The output voltage in differential mode is given by:

$$V_o = (V_2 - V_1)\frac{R_f}{R_1}$$

❑ The sign of the output voltage is:

(1) **negative** if the voltage at the **inverting** input is larger, i.e. $V_1 > V_2$,

(2) **positive** if the voltage at the **non-inverting** input is larger, i.e. $V_2 > V_1$.

❑   *Example*
(a) In the circuit shown below, identify the mode of operation of the amplifier.
(b) What is the output voltage, V_o?

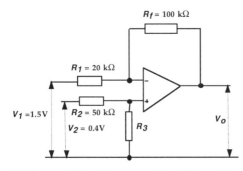

$R_f = 100\ k\Omega$

$R_1 = 20\ k\Omega$

$V_1 = 1.5\ V$ $R_2 = 50\ k\Omega$

$V_2 = 0.4\ V$ R_3

V_o

(a) The amplifier is being used in differential mode. (There are resistors connected to the positive input and there are signals applied to both inputs.)

(b)
$$V_o = (V_2 - V_1)\ \frac{R_f}{R_1} = (0.4 - 1.5) \times \frac{100}{20}$$

$$= -1.1 \times 5 = \textbf{-5.5 V}$$

Monitoring circuits

❑   Many sensors have a resistance which changes with some environmental change, e.g. light intensity, temperature, pressure or strain.

❑   Since the change in resistance is very small, the sensor is used as one arm of an initially balanced Wheatstone bridge.

❑   The change in resistance causes a small voltage change which can be amplified using a differential amplifier. In the circuit shown, R_4, R_5, R_T and R_V form the Wheatstone bridge. R_T is a thermistor and R_V is a variable resistor:

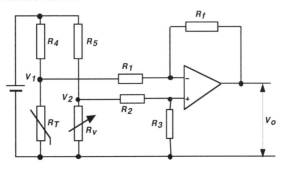

R_f

R_4 R_5

V_1 R_1

V_2 R_2

R_T R_V R_3

V_o

- At a set temperature the bridge is balanced using R_V.

- As the temperature rises, the resistance of the thermistor decreases. This causes V_1 to decrease. $V_2 > V_1$ so V_0 is positive.

- The differential amplifier amplifies this small change in voltage, so the output voltage V_0 gives an indication of the change in temperature sensed by the thermistor.

- The thermistor can be replaced by an LDR, a strain gauge or a pressure sensor, to monitor other physical quantities.

Control circuits

- In many circumstances the differential amplifier is used to control, rather than just monitor, some physical quantity.

- The op-amp will produce a gain in voltage but it only gives a very small output current, not large enough to operate an output device.

- A transistor can amplify a small base current of the order of microamps to produce a collector current of the order of milliamps.

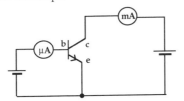

Alternatively, when the base voltage rises above 0.7 V the transistor switches on the collector-emitter circuit.

- By combining the op-amp with transistors, circuits can be built to control other devices.

□ The differential amplifier can be used to switch on a lamp when the output from the amplifier goes positive, i.e. when $V_2 > V_1$:

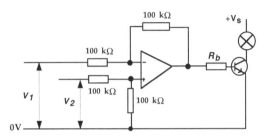

□ In the circuit shown below, the motor can be turned in either forward or reverse directions depending on which of the two voltages V_1 or V_2 is greater:

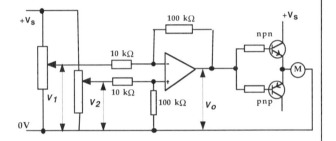

□ There are two transistors, pnp and npn, so that one conducts when the output of the differential amplifier is positive and the other conducts when the output is negative.

□ When $V_2 > V_1$, V_0 is positive.
The npn transistor switches on.
When $V_1 > V_2$, V_0 is negative.
The pnp transistor switches on.
The current in the motor is now reversed.

☐ **Controlling heavier loads**

If necessary, the transistor can close a relay to control very high current devices, i.e. the current required is of the order of amps not milliamps:

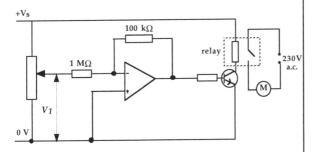

If the motor needs a larger current than the transistor can provide, the transistor can be used to energise the coil of the relay and therefore close the switch.

The 230 V supply is totally separate and can be chosen to give as much current as is required.

NOTE: you will not be expected to draw such circuit diagrams but you may have to explain how they work.

UNIT 3 RADIATION AND MATTER

3.1   Waves

❏   A wave transmits energy.

❏   The **wavelength**, λ, of a wave is the minimum distance in which the wave repeats. It is measured in **metres, m**.

❏   The **frequency, f,** of a wave is the number of waves per second and is measured in **hertz, Hz**.

❏   The **period, T,** of a wave is the time taken for one wave to pass a point or for one wave to be transmitted. It is measured in **seconds, s**.

❏   The **wave speed, v,** is the distance travelled in one second and is measured in **metres per second, m s^{-1}**.

❏   The **amplitude, a,** of a wave is the distance from the centre to the crest or trough.

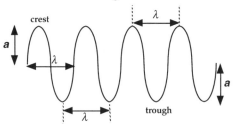

❏   Wave speed, frequency and wavelength are related by the wave equation:

$$v = f\,\lambda$$

❏   The frequency of a wave is the same as the frequency of the source which produces the wave.

❏   The time period in seconds is given by 1/frequency:

$$T = \frac{1}{f} \quad \text{or} \quad f = \frac{1}{T}$$

❏   The energy of the wave depends on its amplitude. The larger the amplitude of the wave, the more energy is being carried by the wave.

❏ Two waves are said to be **in phase** if the same parts of both waves, e.g. crests from each, always arrive at the same point in space at the same time.

❏ Two waves are said to be exactly **out of phase** if opposite parts of both waves, i.e. a crest and a trough, always arrive at the same point in space at the same time.

❏ Two waves are said to be **coherent** if they have the same frequency, wavelength and speed and have a constant phase relationship.

❏ All waves show characteristic behaviour. They will all show **reflection, refraction, diffraction** and **interference**.

❏ **Reflection**
Waves reflect from a surface and obey the law of reflection, i.e. the angle of incidence is equal to the angle of reflection, where both angles are measured to the normal:

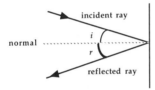

❏ **Refraction**
Waves change direction when passing from one medium into another because the waves move at a different velocity in each of the two media:

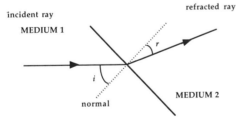

Diffraction

❏ Waves bend round corners. When passing through a gap the waves become bent and if the gap is about the same size as the wavelength, parallel wavefronts emerge as circular wavefronts:

❏ Long wavelengths are diffracted more than short wavelengths.

Interference

❏ Interference occurs when two or more waves are superimposed. The total effect is the sum of the effects caused by the individual waves.

❏ Constructive interference occurs when two waves which are in phase combine at any point:

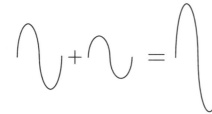

❏ Destructive interference occurs when two waves which are exactly out of phase combine at any point:

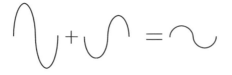

❏ Interference is the test for wave motion.
In order to prove that any form of energy travels as a wave an interference pattern must be shown. This was done for light by Young with the double slit experiment and proved that light is a wave motion.

❑ When two wave trains from coherent sources overlap, an interference pattern is produced:

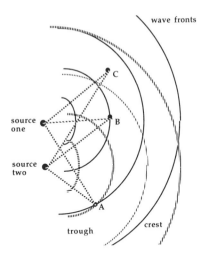

❑ The crests of the waves are shown by the lines and there is a trough halfway between each pair of crests.

❑ At **A**, two crests meet and therefore there is constructive interference. This gives a maximum in the interference pattern, i.e. a crest twice as high.

❑ Point **A** is three wavelengths (3λ) from source one and two wavelengths (2λ) from source two, so the path difference is ($3\lambda - 2\lambda$) = λ.

❑ The general condition for a maximum in the interference pattern is:

> **path difference = n λ** | where **n** is an integer

❑ At **B**, a crest and a trough meet and therefore there is destructive interference. This gives a minimum in the interference pattern, i.e. no displacement if the sources are of equal amplitude.

❑ Point **B** is two wavelengths (2λ) from source one and two and a half wavelengths ($2\frac{1}{2}\lambda$) from source two, so the path difference is ($2\frac{1}{2}\lambda - 2\lambda$) = $\frac{1}{2}\lambda$.

❑ The general condition for a minimum in the

❑ The general condition for a minimum in the interference pattern is:

$$\boxed{\text{path difference} = (n + \tfrac{1}{2})\,\lambda}$$ where **n** = 0 or an integer

i.e. n = 0, 1, 2, 3, 4

❑ At **C**, two troughs overlap and therefore there is constructive interference. This gives a maximum in the interference pattern, a trough twice as deep. For point **C** the path difference is $(3\tfrac{1}{2}\lambda - 2\tfrac{1}{2}\lambda) = \lambda$.

❑ If the points of constructive interference are plotted they form straight lines and the interference pattern of light, when viewed on a screen, shows a series of equally spaced bright lines:

screen | | | | | | lines of
constructive
interference

❑ *Example*
Find the wavelength of microwaves used in the following experiment, if the third off-centre maximum is at **A**.

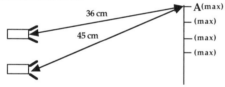

36 cm

45 cm

A(max)
(max)
(max)
(max)

The path difference = 45 - 36 = 9 cm; **n** = 3
For a maxima:

path difference = **n** λ

=> λ = $\dfrac{\text{path difference}}{\textbf{n}}$ = $\dfrac{9}{3}$ = **3 cm**

❑ A laser produces a monochromatic light beam, i.e. one of single frequency and thus single colour.

❑ A laser can be used with a diffraction grating to produce the interference pattern for light. If the laser is red light, the lines of constructive interference are red.

- A grating consists of a number of equally spaced parallel narrow slits. When the grating is placed in front of a monochromatic light source, an interference pattern is produced:

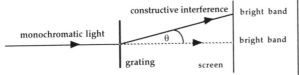

- There will be bright bands caused by constructive interference where:

$$d \sin \theta = n \lambda$$

where d is the separation between each adjacent pair of slits on the grating in m;

    θ is the angle at which constructive interference occurs in degrees,

    λ is the wavelength of the light in m,

    n is an integer.

$n = 0$ gives the central bright band

$n = 1$ gives the first off-centre bright bands (one each side of the centre) called first order.

$n = 2$ gives the second off-centre bright bands (second order) and so on.

- *Example*
  What is the wavelength of light if a diffraction grating with 600 lines per mm, produces the first order line of constructive interference at 17.8°?

- To find the separation, $d = \dfrac{\text{distance}}{\text{number of lines}}$

$$= \frac{1 \times 10^{-3}}{600} \quad \begin{array}{l}\text{(since 1 mm} \\ = 1 \times 10^{-3}\text{ m)}\end{array}$$

$n = 1 \quad \theta = 17.8°$

$d \sin \theta = n \lambda$

$$\Rightarrow \quad \lambda = \frac{d \sin \theta}{n} = \frac{1 \times 10^{-3} \sin 17.8}{600 \times 1} = 5.1 \times 10^{-7}\text{ m}$$

- The wavelength of monochromatic light can be measured by using a diffraction grating of known spacing on a spectrometer. The angle for the first line of constructive interference on each side of the centre is measured. θ is equal to the average of these two angles. Then λ can be found using $d \sin \theta = n \lambda$.

○ A spectrometer produces spectra using either a prism
or a diffraction grating to split the light.
The spectrometer consists of:

a **collimator** - to produce parallel light,
a **telescope** - to focus parallel light,
a **table** - which holds either a diffraction
grating or a prism, to split up the light.

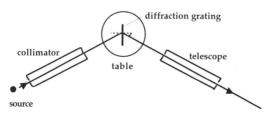

The table has a scale marked round it, so that the
angle through which the telescope has moved can be
measured. (Lasers must not be used as the light is
viewed directly and could be dangerous.)

❏ The approximate values for the wavelength of:

red light	- 700 nm	7.0×10^{-7} m
green light	- 540 nm	5.4×10^{-7} m
blue light	- 490 nm	4.9×10^{-7} m

❏ The white light spectrum produced by a prism is:

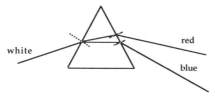

With a prism:

(1) there is one spectrum,
(2) red light is deviated least,
(3) the spectrum is produced by refraction.

❑ The white light spectrum produced by a grating is:

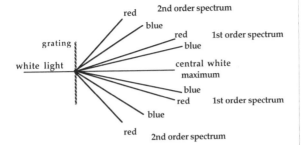

With a grating:
(1) there are pairs of spectra, either side of a central white maximum,
(2) red light is deviated more than blue light,
(3) the spectra are produced by interference.

❑ The central maximum is white because all the wavelengths in white light interfere constructively at this point.

❑ For all other maxima, the grating equation
$d \sin \theta = n\lambda$ applies.

Since: $\lambda_{red} > \lambda_{blue}$

$\sin \theta_{red} > \sin \theta_{blue}$ (n, d constant)

Therefore: $\theta_{red} > \theta_{blue}$ (for same n)

i.e. since the wavelength of red light is greater than the wavelength of blue light, a spectrum is formed for each order, with the red light being deviated more than the blue light.

3.2   Refraction of light

❑   When light passes from medium 1 into medium 2
    the ratio $\dfrac{\sin \theta_1}{\sin \theta_2}$ is a constant:

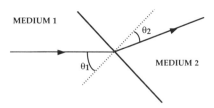

❑   The **absolute refractive index, n** , of a medium is
    given by the ratio:

$$n = \frac{\sin \theta_1}{\sin \theta_2}$$

where θ_1 is the angle in a vacuum (air is used as an
approximation) and θ_2 is the angle in the medium.

❑   The angle in air is always larger than the angle in the
    media.

❑   *Example*
    What is the incident angle in air, if the angle of
    refraction in glass of refactive index 1.4 is 35°?

$$n = \frac{\sin \text{(angle in air)}}{\sin \text{(angle in media)}}$$

=> sin (angle in air)= n x sin (angle in media)

=>   angle in air = $\sin^{-1}$ (1.4 x sin 35) = **53.4°**

**Measurement of the absolute refractive index of glass
for monochromatic light**

❑   A laser can be used to provide monochromatic light:

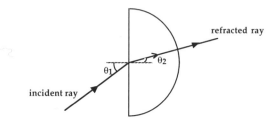

The laser is used to direct a ray of light at a semicircular block as shown. The angles θ_1 and θ_2 are measured.

$$n = \frac{\sin \theta_1}{\sin \theta_2}$$

For accuracy, the ratio can be found for various values of θ_1.

❑ The semicircular block is used so that there is only the single change of direction, as the ray enters the block. Provided that the incident ray is directed at the centre of the straight side, then the refracted ray will always be travelling along a radius. Thus it meets the curved surface at 90° and therefore does not change direction.

❑ The refractive index depends on the frequency of the incident light, i.e. red light and blue light have different frequencies and so have different refractive indices. Therefore a beam of white light is split into a spectrum when passing through a prism.

❑ The frequency of a wave is determined by the source and does not change after leaving the source. Thus the frequency is not affected by a change in medium, i.e. the frequency is the same in water and in air, etc.

❑ Refraction occurs because a wave travels at different speeds in different media.

❑ The refractive index is equal to the ratio of the speeds in the different media. This gives:

$$n = \frac{\sin \theta_1}{\sin \theta_2} = \frac{v_1}{v_2} = \frac{f \lambda_1}{f \lambda_2}$$

Since the frequency is constant, this simplifies to:

Snell's Law

$$n = \frac{\sin \theta_1}{\sin \theta_2} = \frac{v_1}{v_2} = \frac{\lambda_1}{\lambda_2}$$

❑ *Example*

A wave of frequency 6×10^{14} Hz, enters a block at an angle of 50°, and the angle in the block is 36°.
Find the speed and wavelength of the light in the block.

Step 1 Put the information into symbol form.

$$f = 6 \times 10^{14} \text{ Hz}$$
$$\theta_1 = 50^\circ$$
$$\theta_2 = 36^\circ$$
$$v_1 = 3 \times 10^8 \text{ ms}^{-1}$$

Step 2 Choose the correct equations and complete the calculation.

$$n = \frac{\sin \theta_1}{\sin \theta_2} = \frac{\sin 50}{\sin 36} = 1.3$$

$$n = \frac{v_1}{v_2} \Rightarrow v_2 = \frac{v_1}{n}$$
$$= \frac{3 \times 10^8}{1.3}$$
$$= 2.3 \times 10^8 \text{ m s}^{-1}$$

NOTE: the speed in air is always 3×10^8 m s^{-1} and this is the **maximum** value for velocity; thus the velocity of light in any other medium is always less than 3×10^8 m s^{-1}.

$$v_2 = f\lambda \Rightarrow \lambda = \frac{v_2}{f} = \frac{2.3 \times 10^8}{6 \times 10^{14}} = 3.8 \times 10^{-7} \text{ m}$$

❑ When a wave is travelling from an optically more dense to a less dense medium, there is always a maximum angle of incidence, called the **critical angle**, below which the wave can escape from the denser medium, e.g. light travelling from glass into air can only escape provided the angle in the glass is below the critical angle.

❑ At angles of incidence above the critical angle in the optically denser medium, the wave is not refracted out of the medium but totally internally reflected within the medium.

❑ In total internal reflection, all the energy is reflected.

❑ At angles of incidence below the critical angle, in the optically denser material, some of the energy is reflected and some of it is refracted:

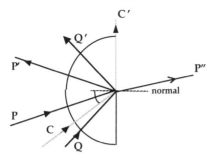

❑ C is the ray which has an angle of incidence equal to the critical angle. It emerges at **90°** in the air and no ray with an angle of incidence in the more dense medium greater than this can emerge into the air.

❑ For a ray such as **P** with an angle of incidence $< \theta_C$, there is both a refracted ray, **P″**, and a reflected ray, **P′**.

❑ For a ray such as **Q** with an angle of incidence $> \theta_C$, there is only the reflected ray, **Q′**, i.e. total internal reflection has taken place.

❑ Total internal reflection is used in optical fibres.

Measurement of the critical angle

❑ Set up a ray box to direct light into a semi-circular block to the centre of the straight edge as shown:

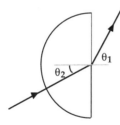

Adjust the value of θ_2 until the refracted ray emerges parallel to the straight side of the block. The value of θ_2 is then equal to the crictical angle, θ_C.

❑ When the angle in the medium is equal to the critical angle, θ_C, the angle in air, θ_1, is 90°.

Applying Snell's law: $\quad n = \dfrac{\sin \theta_1}{\sin \theta_2}$

θ_1 is the angle in air = 90°.

θ_2 is the angle in the medium = θ_C.

Thus: $\quad n = \dfrac{\sin \theta_1}{\sin \theta_2} = \dfrac{\sin 90}{\sin \theta_C}$

But: $\quad \sin 90 = 1$

Thus $\quad \boxed{n = \dfrac{1}{\sin \theta_C}}$ or $\boxed{\sin \theta_C = \dfrac{1}{n}}$

❑ *Example*
What is the critical angle in glass if the refractive index is 1.6?

$$\sin \theta_C = \frac{1}{n} \quad \Rightarrow \quad \theta_C = \sin^{-1}\left(\frac{1}{n}\right)$$

$$= \sin^{-1}\left(\frac{1}{1.6}\right)$$

$$= 38.7°$$

❑ *Example*

Trace the ray through the block shown, made of glass, of refractive index 1.5.

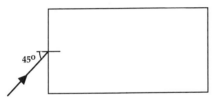

To find the critical angle of this material:

$$\sin\theta_c = \frac{1}{n} \quad => \quad \theta_c = \sin^{-1}\left(\frac{1}{n}\right) = \sin^{-1}\left(\frac{1}{1.5}\right) = 41.8°$$

When the angle in air is 45°:

$$n = \frac{\sin\theta_1}{\sin\theta_2} \quad => \quad \sin\theta_2 = \frac{\sin\theta_1}{n}$$

$$\theta_2 = \sin^{-1}\left(\frac{\sin 45}{1.5}\right) = 28.1°$$

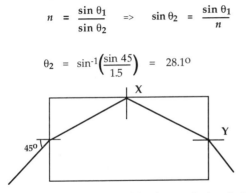

Once the angle in the material has been calculated, the other angles can be found from the geometry of the diagram.

Angles in a triangle add up to 180° and the normal is at right angles to the surface.

At **X**, the angle of incidence is 61.9° which is greater than the critical angle and therefore the light does not escape from the block but undergoes total internal reflection.

At **Y**, the angle in the block is 28.1° and from the original calculation, the equivalent angle in air is 45°.

3.3　Optoelectronics and semiconductors

Intensity of light

❑　The **intensity, I**, at a surface on which radiation falls is the power per unit area:

$$I = \frac{P}{A}$$

where I　is in W m^{-2}
P　is the power in W
A　is the area in m^2

❑　The intensity is inversely proportional to the square of the distance, d, from the source:

$$I = \frac{\text{constant}}{d^2}$$

The constant is different for each situation. This is known as the **inverse square law**.

❑　**Experiment to demonstrate the inverse square law**

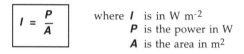

Carry out the experiment in a darkened room, where the lamp is the only source of light. Record the meter reading which is proportional to the intensity, at various known distances:

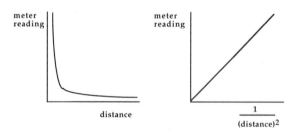

The second graph confirms the inverse square law.

NOTE:　the inverse square law only applies to a point source; the Sun can be considered a point source as we are a very long way from it; a laser is not a point source since it gives a parallel beam.

❑ The relationship between intensity and distance can also be written as:

$$I_1 \, d_1^{\,2} = I_2 \, d_2^{\,2}$$

NOTE: the intensity and the distance can be in any suitable units as long as they are in the same units on both sides.

❑ Example
A point source of light produces an intensity of 5 W m^{-2} at a distance of 50 cm.
What is the intensity at 2.5 m?

NOTE: although the units can vary they must be the same on both sides; therefore change 50 cm to 0.5 m.

Step 1 Put the information into symbol form and change to basic units.

$$I_1 = 5 \text{ W m}^{-2}$$
$$d_1 = 0.5 \text{ m}$$
$$d_2 = 2.5 \text{ m}$$

Step 2 Choose the correct equation and complete the calculation.

$$I_1 \, d_1^{\,2} = I_2 \, d_2^{\,2}$$
$$5 \times (0.5)^2 = I_2 \, (2.5)^2$$
$$\frac{5 \times 0.25}{6.25} = I_2$$
$$I_2 = 0.2 \text{ W m}^{-2}$$

Photoelectric effect
❑ **Photoelectric emission** occurs when electromagnetic radiation of a suitable frequency falls on a clean metal surface and an electron is ejected from the surface.

❑ The photoelectric effect can be demonstrated using a gold leaf electroscope:

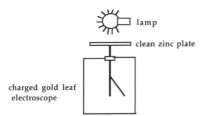

lamp

clean zinc plate

charged gold leaf
electroscope

It was found that :

☐ (1) Only negatively charged electroscopes discharge, showing that this effect is not caused by ionisation but by the emission of electrons from the zinc plate.

☐ (2) Even dim ultra violet radiation of high enough frequency causes the electroscope to discharge because the frequency of the radiation is greater than the threshold frequency, f_o, for the zinc plate.

☐ (3) No matter how intense the visible light source used, even a laser, no electrons leave the surface, because the frequency of the light is less than the threshold frequency, f_o, for the zinc plate.

☐ (4) The rate at which the electroscope discharges depends on the distance the ultra violet radiation is from the zinc plate. This is because the rate at which photoelectrons are produced is proportional to the intensity of the radiation at the zinc plate.

☐ Einstein explained this by suggesting that electromagnetic radiation sometimes behaves more like particles than waves.
He called these particles of radiation, **photons**.

☐ Each photon can be thought of as a small bundle of waves.

☐ A beam of radiation can be thought of as a stream of photons:

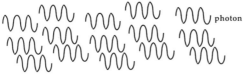

photon

parallel beam of radiation ⟶

☐ A photon has energy given by:

$$E = h f$$

where E is the energy in J
f is the frequency of radiation in Hz
h is Planck's constant (6.63×10^{-34} J s)

❏ A more intense light produces more photons per second than a dim light:

$$I = N h f$$

where I is the intensity in W m^{-2}

N is the number of photons per second per square metre

h is Planck's constant (6.63 x 10^{-34} J s)

f is the frequency of radiation in Hz

❏ When a photon is absorbed, **all** of its energy is given to **one** electron.

❏ The photoelectric effect occurs if an electron can gain enough energy from one photon of the incident radiation to escape from the particular metal.

❏ The minimum energy needed by an electron to escape from a metal is called the **work function**.

❏ As the energy of a photon depends on the frequency, f, the minimum required frequency (work function) for electron escape is called the threshold frequency, f_o.

$$\text{work function} = h f_o$$

❏ Every metal has a different value for the work function.

❏ If the incident photon has a frequency higher than f_o, it has energy which is greater than the work function. The extra energy is given to the electron as kinetic energy.

$$
\begin{array}{rcl}
\text{energy of} & = & \text{work function} + \text{kinetic energy} \\
\text{incident photon} & & \text{of electron} \\
h f & = & h f_o + E_k
\end{array}
$$

Properties of photoelectric effect

❏ (1) Photoelectric emission only occurs when the frequency of the incident radiation is greater than some threshold frequency, f_o, which depends on the nature of the surface.

❏ (2) For frequencies smaller than f_o, an increase in the intensity of radiation will not cause photoelectric emission.

❏ (3) For frequencies greater than f_o, the photoelectric current produced by monochromatic (single frequency, single colour) radiation is proportional to the intensity of the radiation at the surface.

❏   *Example*

If the work function of lead is 6.4 x 10^{-19} J
(a) find the threshold frequency for lead,
(b) calculate the kinetic energy of electrons emitted
    when radiation of frequency 2.6 x10^{15} Hz falls on lead,
(c) state whether the photoelectric effect will occur with
    light of wavelength 400 nm.

Step 1   Put the information into symbol form.

$$\text{work function} = 6.4 \times 10^{-19} \text{ J}$$
$$f = 2.6 \times 10^{15} \text{ Hz}$$
$$\lambda = 400 \text{ nm} = 4 \times 10^{-7} \text{ m}$$
$$v = 3 \times 10^{8} \text{ m s}^{-1}$$

Step 2   Choose the correct equations and complete
the calculations.

(a) $\text{work function} = h\,f_o$

$$\Rightarrow \quad f_o = \frac{\text{work function}}{h}$$

$$= \frac{6.4 \times 10^{-19}}{6.63 \times 10^{-34}}$$

$$= 9.65 \times 10^{14} \text{ Hz}$$

(b) $h\,f = h\,f_o + E_k$

$$\Rightarrow E_k = h\,f - h\,f_o$$

$$= h\,(f - f_o)$$

$$= 6.63 \times 10^{-34}\,(2.6 \times 10^{15} - 9.65 \times 10^{14})$$

$$= 6.63 \times 10^{-34}\,(1.635 \times 10^{15})$$

$$= 1.08 \times 10^{-18} \text{ J}$$

(c) $v = f\lambda \quad \Rightarrow \quad f = \dfrac{v}{\lambda}$

$$= \frac{3 \times 10^{8}}{4 \times 10^{-7}}$$

$$= 7.5 \times 10^{14} \text{ Hz}$$

Since this frequency is less than f_o, no
photoemission takes place.

Energy levels

❑ In an atom, the electrons orbit the nucleus. Only certain orbits are allowed and this means that the energy of the electron can only have certain allowed values:

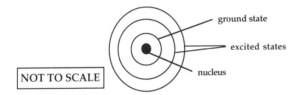

NOT TO SCALE

ground state

excited states

nucleus

❑ In the smallest orbit, nearest the nucleus, the electron has the least energy and is said to be in the **ground state.**

❑ When an electron gains energy from any outside source it may be able to move into a higher energy level and is said to be **excited.**

❑ The electron can only absorb energy if it is the right amount to take the electron to another allowed energy level.

❑ If the electron gains enough energy, then it can reach the top level, which is equivalent to leaving the atom altogether. This is called the **ionisation level.**

❑ The energy levels for hydrogen can be represented by an energy level diagram:

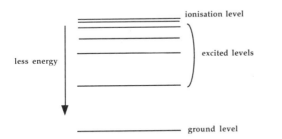

ionisation level

less energy

excited levels

ground level

NOTE: energy levels are negative by convention; the minus signs can be ignored as only the size of the change in energy, ΔE, will require to be calculated.

Spectra

❑ **Emission spectra** are produced when light is given out, by electrons moving down in energy level:

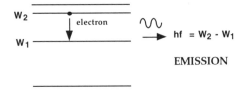

EMISSION

❑ **Absorption spectra** are produced when the electrons absorb energy and move up in energy level:

ABSORPTION

❑ **Continuous spectra** are produced by solids, liquids and high pressure gases.

❑ **Line spectra** are produced by low pressure gases.

❑ Since electrons can only be in specific energy levels, changes between these levels give only particular values of ΔE, and therefore particular frequencies ($E = h f$). Therefore the idea of energy levels leads to line spectra.

❑ An **emission line** in a spectrum occurs when an electron makes a transition between an excited energy level W_2 and a lower energy level W_1, where:

$$\boxed{W_2 - W_1 \;=\; h f}$$

❑ The emission line will appear brighter if more electrons make that particular transition.

❑ An **absorption line** in a spectrum occurs when an electron in energy level W_1 absorbs radiation of energy $h f$ and is excited to energy level W_2, where:

$$\boxed{W_2 - W_1 \;=\; h f}$$

❑ The electron can only absorb the energy from radiation if the radiation is of the right frequency to move it to an allowed energy level.

❑ The absorption spectrum of an element consists of black lines on a continuous spectrum, in exactly the same positions as the bright lines of the emission spectrum.

❑ Absorption lines occur in the **Sun's spectrum** because gases in the outer part of the Sun absorb light of particular frequencies. The white light is produced in the centre of the Sun but after passing through the gas layer certain frequencies are missing. This gives dark lines which correspond to the frequencies which have been absorbed by the gases in the Sun's atmosphere. This allows the elements which make up the Sun to be determined. The dark lines are called **Fraunhofer lines**.

❑ *Example*
The energies of three energy levels for hydrogen are -2.4×10^{-19} J, -5.4×10^{-19} J and -21.8×10^{-19} J.
(a) What is the highest frequency line produced?
(b) Will light of wavelength $\lambda = 6.63 \times 10^{-7}$ m be absorbed?

Step 1 Put the information into symbol form.

$$\lambda = 6.63 \times 10^{-7} \text{ m}$$
$$v = 3 \times 10^8 \text{ ms}^{-1}$$
$$h = 6.63 \times 10^{-34} \text{ J}$$

(a) The highest frequency will come from the greatest energy change:

$$\Delta E = (21.8 - 2.4) \times 10^{-19} \text{ J}$$
$$= 19.4 \times 10^{-19} \text{ J}$$

Step 2 Choose the correct equations and complete the calculation.

(a) $\Delta E = h f$
$\Rightarrow f = \dfrac{\Delta E}{h} = \dfrac{19.4 \times 10^{-19}}{6.63 \times 10^{-34}} = 2.93 \times 10^{15}$ Hz

NOTE: this highest frequency goes with the smallest wavelength.

(b) $f = \dfrac{v}{\lambda} = \dfrac{3 \times 10^8}{6.63 \times 10^{-7}} = 4.52 \times 10^{14}$ Hz

$E = h f = 4.52 \times 10^{14} \times 6.63 \times 10^{-34}$
$= 3 \times 10^{-19}$ J

This is the size of the energy gap between the top two energy levels. Therefore an electron in level 2 will absorb this wavelength and move to level 3.

Lasers

❑ **Spontaneous emission** is a random process. An electron drops down in energy level but the time at which this occurs can not be predicted, just as the time at which a particular radioactive nucleus will decay cannot be predicted.

❑ **Stimulated emission** occurs when a photon of the correct energy, **h f**, causes an electron in an excited level to drop down to a lower energy level, emitting a second photon of the same energy.

❑ In stimulated emission, the incident radiation and the emitted radiation are in phase and travel in the same direction:

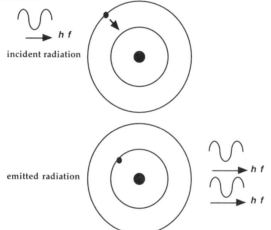

incident radiation

emitted radiation

❑ This occurs in a **LASER** , which stands for Light Amplification by Stimulated Emission of Radiation. These two photons can go on to produce the same effect in other excited atoms, producing a sort of chain reaction.

❑ In a laser the conditions are such that the light beam gains more energy by stimulated emission than it loses by absorption.

❑ Laser light is:
  (1) monochromatic,
      i.e. single colour since all photons have the same frequency,
  (2) coherent,
      i.e. all photons are in phase,
  (3) intense,
      i.e. all photons are coherent and concentrated in a small area.

❑ The laser has plane mirrors at each end. Only light parallel with the sides is amplified. Photons going in other directions are lost. At one end there is a fully silvered mirror which reflects all the photons while at the other end is a half silvered mirror which allows some of the laser light to escape.

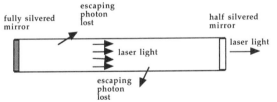

Thus the mirrors reinforce the laser light in one direction.

❑ A beam of laser light with a power of only 0.1 mW may cause damage to the eye, even although a 100 W light bulb does not. The intensity of the laser beam is given by:

$$I = \frac{P}{A}$$

where I is the intensity in W m^{-2}
P is the power in W
A is the area in m^2

The diameter of a laser beam is typically 1 mm.
Thus the intensity of the laser light is found by:

$$I = \frac{P}{A} = \frac{0.1}{\pi\, r^2} = \frac{0.1 \times 10^{-3}}{3.14 \times (0.5 \times 10^{-3})^2} = 127\ \text{W m}^{-2}$$

The beam remains approximately the same size so the intensity remains constant, about the same 10 m away (although school lasers will spread out a little).

By comparison, the light from a 100 W bulb covers the surface of a sphere (area = $4\,\pi\, r^2$) so at 10 m the intensity is found by:

$$I = \frac{P}{A} = \frac{100}{4\,\pi\, r^2} = \frac{100}{4 \times 3.14 \times 100} = 8 \times 10^{-2}\ \text{W m}^{-2}$$

Thus the laser gives much higher intensity.

❑ The parallel beam of the laser is small enough to pass through the pupil of the eye, so that all the light reaches the retina causing damage.

❏ Materials can be divided into three broad categories according to their electrical properties.

❏ **Conductors** have many 'free' electrons available to constitute a current, e.g. metals such as copper, silver.

❏ **Insulators** have very few 'free' electrons which cannot move easily and therefore offer a high resistance, e.g. rubber, plastic.

❏ **Semiconductors** are materials which behave like insulators when pure but can be made to conduct by the addition of impurities, e.g. silicon (Si), germanium (Ge).

❏ Doping is the addition of an impurity to a pure semiconductor.

❏ Doping reduces the resistance of the semiconductor.

❏ Silicon has four valence electrons in the outer shell. These bond with other atoms to give a lattice with no spare charge carriers. This is an insulator.

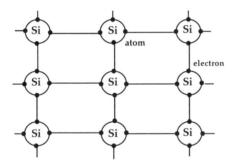

◯ *As the temperature rises, a few electrons escape from their atoms. They leave behind a 'hole'. Both electrons and holes can constitute a current, so the resistance of the semiconductor falls.*

□ **n-type semiconductor**
If an impurity such as phosphorus is added to the
silicon, phosphorus has five electrons in its outer shell.
Only four of them are required to bond the atoms which
leaves one free electron for each phosphorus atom:

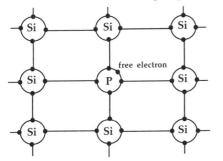

These free electrons can form a current. Since these are
negative charge carriers this is an **n-type** semiconductor.

□ **p-type semiconductor**
If an impurity, such as boron, with only three electrons
in the outer shell is added to the silicon, there is a **'hole'**,
i.e. a missing electron:

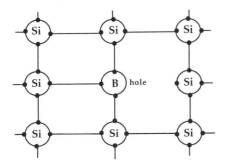

This hole can move through the lattice, effectively
carrying **positive** charge so this makes a **p-type**
semiconductor.

□ Both p-type and n-type silicon are electrically neutral
overall.

○ *As the temperature increases, some electrons will
leave silicon atoms, leaving a hole behind. This gives:
p-type - majority charge carrier holes, minority electrons;
n-type - majority charge carrier electrons, minority holes.*

○ *The more doping that takes place the more charge
carriers there are. Each impurity atom gives one charge
carrier.*

❑ **p-n junction diode**
This can be produced by doping the same piece of silicon with different impurities. Although both sides of the material are electrically neutral, some electrons and holes move across the junction and combine:

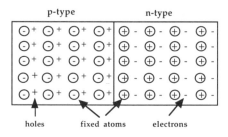

❑ Since the electrons and the holes have combined, there are no free charge carriers just around the junction. This is called the depletion layer. However there are charges on the atoms as shown and these fixed charges stop any further movement of charge carriers across the junction:

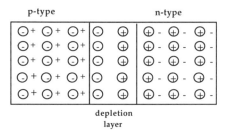

❑ This is equivalent to having a potential difference across the junction which opposes any further movement of electrons (from n-type to p-type) and holes (from p-type to n-type).

❑ Applying a voltage to a semiconductor device is called **biasing.**

There are two ways to apply the voltage:

❑ (1) The cell is connected

with **positive** to p-type
        negative to n-type.
This is **forward biasing**; the diode conducts.

❑ (2) The cell is connected the opposite way round,

i.e. with **positive** to n-type
        negative to p-type.
This is **reverse biasing**; the diode does not conduct.

□ **Forward biasing**

In order to overcome the potential barrier due to the depletion layer and allow the charge carriers to move across the junction, a larger potential must be applied in the opposite direction:

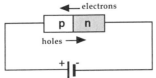

In a forward biased diode, electrons from the n-type are attracted to the positive battery terminal. They pass through the junction and flow round the circuit as shown above. Holes are attracted to the negative terminal and flow round the circuit, in the opposite direction to the electrons, as in the diagram above. The depletion layer is reduced and the diode conducts.

□ **Reverse biasing**

This time the potential of the cell reinforces the potential due to the depletion layer and the diode will not conduct:

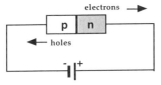

Electrons attracted to the positive terminal and holes attracted to the negative terminal move away from the junction. Therefore the depletion layer becomes wider and the diode does not conduct.

□ **Light Emitting Diode**

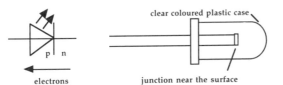

The LED has a p-n junction very close to the surface. In use this is forward biased. When holes and electrons are crossing the junction, some of them meet and recombine, giving out energy. When this happens the energy can be given out as a photon of light. The recombination energy of the electron-hole pair is equal to hf, where f is the frequency of the emitted light.

The photodiode

❑ In a photodiode, the p-n junction is still very close to the surface and encased in clear plastic but this time electron-hole pairs are produced when light falls on the junction. Each photon gives up its energy and produces one electron-hole pair.

The circuit symbol is:

There are two ways to use a photodiode:

(1) Photovoltaic mode

❑ In this case the photodiode can be used to supply power to a load, i.e. it acts as a battery. This is the basis of solar cells. When the photon lands on the junction its energy is absorbed and produces electron-hole pairs, and thus a voltage. The more intense the light is, the more photons absorbed and therefore the higher the voltage:

❑ The voltage is proportional to the light intensity and the photodiode reacts very quickly. It can be used to detect changes in light levels, e.g. in optical fibres.

(2) Photoconductive mode

❑ In this case the photodiode is used as a light sensor. The photodiode is reverse biased and would not normally conduct:

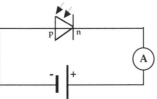

❑ The reverse leakage current of a photodiode is directly proportional to the intensity of light falling on it.

❑ As long as the reverse biasing voltage is less than the breakdown voltage of the photodiode, the reverse leakage current is also almost independent of the reverse biasing voltage.

❑ The switching action of a reverse-biased photodiode is extremely fast.

○ *When light falls on the junction, electron-hole pairs are produced which will form a current. Thus the resistance of the junction is reduced and it can act as an LDR.*

❑ The MOSFET is a **M**etal **O**xide **S**emiconductor **F**ield **E**ffect **T**ransistor.

❑ There are two types of MOSFET, n-channel and p-channel.

❑ An n-channel enhancement MOSFET has the following structure:

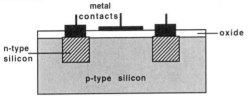

A block of p-type silicon, called the substrate, has two n-type regions implanted in it as shown. A layer of silicon dioxide is grown across the surface and then two holes are etched in this to give a metal contact to each n-type area. There is a third metal contact on the oxide between the two n-type areas.

❑ The contacts to the n-type areas are called the source and the drain. The contact over the oxide is called the gate:

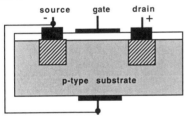

❑ The **source** is the n-type implant connected to the p-type substrate.

❑ The **drain** is the n-type implant **not** connected to the substrate.

❑ The **gate** is the terminal insulated from the substrate by the oxide layer.

❑ There is no current between the source and the drain because there are two reverse biased p-n junctions. These are the junctions between the source and the substrate and the junction between the substrate and the drain. The MOSFET is OFF.

❑ The symbol for an n-channel MOSFET is:

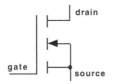

○ *The symbol for a p-channel MOSFET is the same apart from the arrow, which points the other way.*

❑ When the MOSFET is in use, the gate is made positive and this opens a channel for electrons between the source and the drain.

❑ The channel is called an n-channel because it is formed by electrons.

○ *The positive charge on the gate attracts electrons from the p-type substrate to the surface. The electrons are always present as minority charge carriers in the p-type material, formed by thermal effects causing electron-hole pairs. This gives a channel of n-type material between the source and drain as long as there is sufficient positive charge on the gate.*

❑ The drain is always more positive than the source.

❑ When the gate forms the n-channel, current can flow between the source and the drain. The MOSFET is ON.

MOSFET Circuits

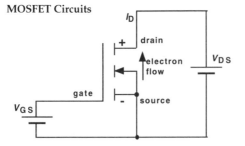

❑ The potential difference across the source and drain is V_{DS}. (The drain is more positive than the source).

❑ The potential difference across the source and gate is V_{GS}. (The gate is more positive than the source).

❏ The current in the drain-source circuit is called the drain current, I_D.

❏ The gate voltage, V_{GS}, has a minimum value called the threshold voltage. Below this the channel does not open. It is typically about 2 V.

Transistor switch

❏

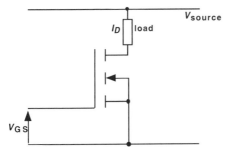

❏ A gate voltage greater than the threshold voltage applied to the gate will turn on the transistor. This gives a drain current in the load resistor.

❏ The load resistor could be any device such as a lamp, buzzer, motor, heater, relay, etc.

Transistor amplifier

❏ An n-channel MOSFET can be used as an amplifier:

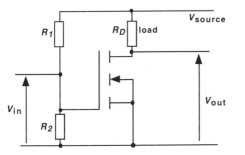

❏ R_1 and R_2 are used to ensure the transistor is switched on.

❏ The voltage gain of the amplifier is given by $\dfrac{V_{out}}{V_{in}}$.

3.4   Nuclear reactions

Rutherford's experiment

❑   Rutherford's experiment confirmed the view that the
    atom consists of a central nucleus with a relatively
    small diameter containing most of the mass. It was
    carried out by Geiger and Marsden and involved firing
    alpha particles at gold foil in a vacuum:

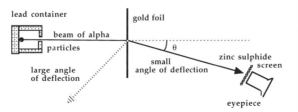

The alpha particles were detected by the scintillations, i.e.
flashes of light which they caused on the zinc sulphide
screen.

❑   The main results were:

  (1) Most of the alpha particles passed straight through
     the foil with little or no deviation.

  (2) A few were deviated through fairly large angles, up
     to 90°.

  (3) A very few were deviated through angles of more
     than 90°, i.e. they bounced back.

❑   Rutherford concluded that:

  (1) Since even very thin foil is about 100 atoms thick,
     result (1) shows that most of the atom must be
     empty space for so many alpha particles to pass
     straight through.

  (2) Since some alpha particles bounce back, most of the
     mass and all the positive charge must be
     concentrated in a very small volume; this is the
     nucleus.

❑   This gave Rutherford's model of the atom:

  (1) The nucleus has a relatively small diameter
     compared with that of the atom.

  (2) Most of the mass of the atom is concentrated in the
     nucleus.

Structure of the nucleus

❑ The number of protons in the nucleus is known as the **atomic number** or **proton number (Z)**.
Since atoms are electrically neutral, this is equal to the number of electrons orbiting the nucleus.

❑ The total number of **nucleons** (protons and neutrons) in the nucleus is the **mass number** or **nucleon number (A)**.

❑ This is normally written: $^{A}_{Z}X$

where **X** is the chemical symbol for the element.

❑ Every element has a different atomic number. Elements are arranged in order of increasing atomic number in the Periodic Table.

❑ Nuclei with the same atomic number can have different mass numbers, i.e. they have the same number of protons but a different number of neutrons,

e.g. $^{20}_{10}Ne$ $^{22}_{10}Ne$.

These nuclei, sometimes written as neon 20 and neon 22, are called **isotopes**.

❑ It is also possible for atoms of different elements to have the same mass number,

e.g. $^{212}_{83}Bi$ $^{212}_{82}Pb$.

❑ The relative masses and charges of the proton, neutron and electron are:

Particle	Mass	Charge	Symbol
proton	1	+1	$^{1}_{1}p$
neutron	1	0	$^{1}_{0}n$
electron	1/1840	-1	$^{0}_{-1}e$

❑ The mass of the electron is often taken as zero.

❑ A **radionuclide** (or **radioisotope**) is an isotope which decays radioactively.

❏ An **alpha particle** (symbol α) is a helium nucleus. Therefore it has an atomic number of 2 and a mass number of 4.

❏ In **alpha decay**, the daughter isotope is a different element:

$$^A_Z X \longrightarrow \, ^{A-4}_{Z-2} Y + \, ^4_2 He$$

❏ A **beta particle** (symbol β) is a high energy electron from the nucleus. It is created when a neutron decays into an electron and a proton:

$$^1_0 n \longrightarrow \, ^1_1 p + \, ^0_{-1} e$$

❏ In **beta decay**, the daughter isotope is a different element:

$$^A_Z X \longrightarrow \, ^A_{Z+1} Y + \, ^0_{-1} e$$

❏ In **gamma decay** (symbol γ) there is no change in the isotope. The nucleus just loses energy in the form of electromagnetic radiation.

❏ Thus radioactive decay can result in the atomic number going down by two (alpha decay) or up by one (beta decay). If the atomic number appears to have gone down by one, then there have been two successive decays, alpha then beta, or beta then alpha .

❏ *Example 1*
Identify the particle emitted at each stage in the decay series shown:

$$^{235}_{92} U \underset{(a)}{\longrightarrow} \, ^{231}_{90} Th \underset{(b)}{\longrightarrow} \, ^{231}_{91} Pa \underset{(c)}{\longrightarrow} \, ^{227}_{89} Ac$$

(a) The atomic number has gone down 2 - **alpha**.
(b) The atomic number has gone up 1 - **beta**.
(c) The atomic number has gone down 2 - **alpha**.

❏ *Example 2*
In the following decay series identify the missing isotopes.

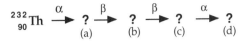

$$^{232}_{90}\text{Th} \xrightarrow{\alpha} \underset{(a)}{?} \xrightarrow{\beta} \underset{(b)}{?} \xrightarrow{\beta} \underset{(c)}{?} \xrightarrow{\alpha} \underset{(d)}{?}$$

In α - emission, the mass number goes down four and the atomic number by two.
Therefore:

the new mass number is 232 - 4 = 228
the new atomic number is 90 - 2 = 88

From the Periodic Table the element with atomic number 88 is radium. Isotope (a) is $^{228}_{88}\text{Ra}$.

β - emission leaves the mass number unchanged and takes the atomic number up one from 88 to 89. Isotope (b) is $^{228}_{89}\text{Ac}$, actinium.

In the same way the rest of the decay series can be deduced:

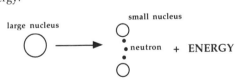

$$^{232}_{90}\text{Th} \xrightarrow{\alpha} ^{228}_{88}\text{Ra} \xrightarrow{\beta} ^{228}_{89}\text{Ac} \xrightarrow{\beta} ^{228}_{90}\text{Th} \xrightarrow{\alpha} ^{224}_{88}\text{Ra}$$

NOTE : in both alpha and beta decay there may be gamma radiation given off as well, although this cannot be concluded from a study of the isotopes formed.

Fission and fusion

❏ In **fission**, a large nucleus splits into two nuclei of smaller mass with the release of several neutrons and energy:

large nucleus   small nucleus

neutron   +   **ENERGY**

❏ This fission can be **spontaneous**, occuring at random with a fixed half life, or stimulated.
In **stimulated** fission, the nucleus is hit by an incident neutron causing it to undergo fission.

❏ If the mass of the nucleus before the fission and the mass of all the components after the collision are accurately measured, there is always some loss of mass.

❑ This lost mass is converted into energy according to Einstein's equation:

$$E = mc^2$$

where E is the energy in J
m is the mass in kg
c is the velocity of light
$(3 \times 10^8 \text{ m s}^{-1})$

❑ *Example*

A uranium isotope decays as shown:

$$^{235}_{92}U + ^{1}_{0}n \rightarrow ^{98}_{42}Mo + ^{136}_{54}Xe + 2\,^{1}_{0}n + 4\,^{0}_{-1}e$$

The mass of $^{235}_{92}U$ = 3.9×10^{-25} kg

The mass of $^{98}_{42}Mo$ = 1.63×10^{-25} kg

The mass of $^{136}_{54}Xe$ = 2.25×10^{-25} k

The mass of $^{1}_{0}n$ = 1.67×10^{-27} kg

How much energy is released?

Total mass before fission = $3.9 \times 10^{-25} + 1.67 \times 10^{-27}$
= 3.9167×10^{-25} kg

Total mass after fission =
$1.63 \times 10^{-25} + 2.25 \times 10^{-25} + 2 \times 1.67 \times 10^{-27}$
= 3.9134×10^{-25} kg
(the mass of an electron is so small it is ignored)

Lost mass = 3.3×10^{-28} kg

$$E = mc^2 = 3.3 \times 10^{-28} \times 9 \times 10^{16} = 2.97 \times 10^{-11} \text{ J}$$

❑ Each individual fission only gives a small amount of energy but in a nuclear reactor there will be a great many fissions taking place per second, thus producing a large amount of energy.

❑ This energy is in the form of kinetic energy of the particles.

❑   In a **chain reaction** the neutrons produced in the fission go on to cause further fissions.

❑   This process is uncontrolled in an atom bomb. In a nuclear reactor, the number of neutrons are controlled, so that on average only one neutron produced in a fission goes on to cause a further fission.

❑   In **fusion**, two small nuclei combine to form one larger nucleus and energy:

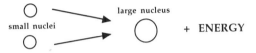

small nuclei   large nucleus   + **ENERGY**

❑   If the mass before the fusion and mass after the fusion are accurately measured, there is always some missing mass.

❑   The missing mass is changed into energy according to Einstein's equation:

$$E = m\,c^2$$

❑   This energy becomes the kinetic energy of the larger nucleus.

❑   Two isotopes of hydrogen, ^2_1H (**deuterium**) and ^3_1H (**tritium**), are used to produce fusion. Deuterium is about 1/500th of all hydrogen and so is available from sea water in large quantities.

❑   If fusion reactors can be established there will be unlimited energy without dangerous radioactive waste. The trouble is that to make the small nuclei join together, as they do in the Sun, temperatures similar to those in the Sun have to be established. Since this is very high, any container will melt and containment of the very hot material becomes a major problem. Scientists have yet to solve this problem and produce energy from fusion on a practical scale.

3.5   Dosimetry and safety

❑   **The activity, *A*,** of a radioactive source is measured in **becquerels, Bq**, where 1 Bq is one atom decaying per second.

❑   The activity of a radioactive source decreases with time.

❑   The average activity *A* of a quantity of radionuclide is a measure of the rate at which it decays:

$$A = \frac{N}{t}$$

where **N** is the number of nuclei decaying
        t is the time in s

❑   *Example*
    If there are 5×10^7 decays from a particular source in 25 s, what is the activity?

$$A = \frac{N}{t} = \frac{5 \times 10^7}{25} = 2 \times 10^6 \, Bq = \mathbf{2\ MBq}$$

❑   The decay of an individual atom is a totally random event and cannot be predicted.

❑   However the time taken for half the atoms, in a sample of a particular material, to decay is always the same. This is called the **half life**.

❑   The half life is the time taken for the activity of a sample to drop by half.

❑   When calculating the half life the count rate corrected for background count rate should be used. This is obtained by estimating the background count rate and deducting this from all values.

❑   The background radiation can be estimated from the final level of an Activity / Time graph:

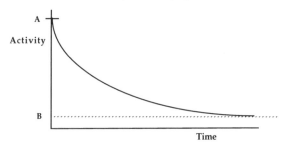

❑ The initial activity **A** comes from both the source and from the background, **B**.
Therefore the activity due to the source alone is: **A - B**
After one half life the activity due to the source will become: $\dfrac{(A - B)}{2}$

But the activity actually measured will still come from both the background and the source.

Thus the total activity will then be: $\dfrac{(A - B)}{2} + B$

Absorption of radiation

❑ The effects of absorbed radiation depends not only on the amount of the radiation but also on the size of the object which absorbs it.

❑ The **absorbed dose, D**, is the energy, **E**, absorbed per unit mass, **m**, of the absorbing material. It is measured in **grays, Gy**, where $1\ \text{Gy} = 1\ \text{J kg}^{-1}$.

$$D = \frac{E}{m}$$

where **D** is in Gy
E is in J
m is in kg

❑ The risk of biological harm from an exposure to radiation depends on:

(1) the absorbed dose,

(2) the kind of radiation, e.g. α, β, γ, or slow neutrons,

(3) the body organs or tissues exposed.

❑ The **dose equivalent, H**, which is measured in **sieverts, Sv**, takes into account the type and energy of the radiation. The same dose equivalent in **Sv** always gives the same biological effect.

❑ Each type of radiation is allocated a **quality factor, Q**. This is just a number which compares the biological effect of the radiation.

❑ The dose equivalent is given by the absorbed dose multiplied by the quality factor:

$$H = D\ Q$$

where **D** is in Gy
Q is the quality factor
H is in Sv

❑ Since the quality factor is a non-dimensional number, the units of **H** are the same as those of **D**.
Therefore one sievert is also equal to one joule per kilogram, $(1\ \text{Sv} = 1\ \text{J kg}^{-1})$.

❏ The **dose equivalent rate,** $\dot{H}$ (H-dot), is given by:

$$\dot{H} = \frac{H}{t}$$ where H is in Sv

$\dot{H}$ can be in Sv s^{-1}, etc. depending on the units of time.

○ *The **absorbed dose rate,** $\dot{D}$ (D-dot), is given by the absorbed dose per unit time:*

$$\dot{D} = \frac{D}{t}$$ *where D is in Gy*

The time can be in years, hours, minutes or seconds as appropriate. This will change the units of $\dot{D}$, which can be in Gy yr^{-1}, Gy hr^{-1}, Gy min^{-1} or Gy s^{-1}.

❏ When calculating the overall effect of radiation from various sources, the dose equivalent of each source must be calculated before adding up to find the total. This is true whether working in terms of dose or dose rate.

❏ *Example*
A worker is exposed to 15 mGy of γ - radiation, 400 μGy of fast neutrons and 600 μGy of α - particles in the course of a year. What is his total dose equivalent?

The quality factors are: γ - radiation   -   1
                        fast neutrons   -   10
                        α - particles   -   20

H = D Q

γ - radiation = 15 x 10^{-3} x 1   = 15 x 10^{-3} Sv
fast neutrons = 400 x 10^{-6} x 10 = 4 x 10^{-3} Sv
α - radiation = 600 x 10^{-6} x 20 = 12 x 10^{-3} Sv

Total dose equivalent   = **31 x 10^{-3} Sv**
                               (31 mSv)

❏ Different tissues in the body vary in their susceptibility to damage from radiation.

❏ The **effective dose equivalent** is measured in sieverts and takes account of the type of tissue. It is used to indicate the risk to health from exposure to ionising radiation.

❑ We are exposed to continual background radiation.

❑ The average annual effective dose equivalent for a person in the UK from natural sources (cosmic, terrestrial and internal radiation) is about 2 mSv.

❑ Typical annual dose equivalent values for various sources of background radiation are:

Cosmic radiation	0.3 mSv
Radioactivity from rocks, soil, buildings	0.3 mSv
Radioactivity present in the human body	0.4 mSv
Inhaled radon and daughter products	1.0 mSv
Total exposure	**2.0 mSv**

❑ Cosmic rays are radiations from outer space, consisting of many different type of particles and electromagnetic radiation. The atmosphere absorbs much of the radiation and the dose equivalent varies with altitude. High flying planes can be exposed to much higher levels of radiation from cosmic rays and may sometimes move to a lower level if the cosmic radiation is at a particularly high level.

❑ Rocks, soils and building materials, especially granite, often contain radioactive material. Aberdeen, 'The Granite City' has a dose equivalent of about 1.7 mSv annually, while Kerala in India has thorium in the soil and has an annual dose equivalent of about 20 mSv.

❑ Human radioactivity comes from both potassium and carbon in cells and from various isotopes, which are incorporated into our bones, from the food that we eat.

❑ The main source of exposure comes from radon and its daughter products. Radon can accumulate in buildings from the material of which they are made.

❑ Artificial sources of radiation such as medical X - rays, nuclear reactors, etc. can add about another 0.28 mSv per year.

Exposure limits have been set for exposure to radiation:

❑ (1) For the **general public**, the limit is **5 mSv** in addition to background in any one year and an average of **1 mSv** over the long term

❑ (2) For **workers** who are exposed to radiation during their employment, the limit is **50 mSv** per year in addition to background. (These may include pilots, medical workers, physics teachers, etc. as well as those working at nuclear plants!)

- ❑ The exposure from any particular source can be limited by shielding, i.e. by placing some absorbing material between the source and the people.

- ❑ Suitable absorbing materials are lead and thick concrete.

Experiment to find the effect of varying the thickness of an absorber

❑

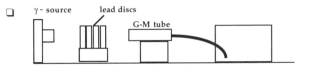

The count rate is measured in the absence of the source over 2 minutes to find the background count per second. The count rate is then measured with the source and no lead discs, then with one lead disc, two, etc. Again, the count per second is found by measuring the count over two minutes. This allows for the random effect of radioactivity.

- ❑ The count rate, corrected for the recorded background reading, is plotted against the absorber thickness:

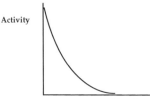

The count rate decreases as the thickness of the absorber increases.

- ❑ The **half value thickness** of an absorber is the thickness of absorber which reduces the intensity of the beam of γ - rays by half.

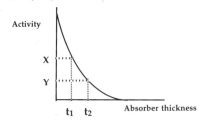

- ❑ Choose any initial activity, **X** , and find the equivalent thickness, t_1, At half the count rate, **Y** , find the equivalent thickness, t_2.
  The half value thickness is $t_2 - t_1$.

❑ As with half life, the half value thickness is independent of the starting count rate.

❑ The half value thickness will depend on the activity of the source, the energy of the radiation and the type of absorber.

❑ *Example*
The dose equivalent rate for a gamma source is 256 mSv hr^{-1}. If the half value thickness of lead for this radiation is 30 mm, how thick must the shield be to reduce the dose equivalent rate to a safe 1 mSv hr^{-1}?

256 ➤ 128 ➤ 64 ➤ 32 ➤ 16 ➤ 8 ➤ 4 ➤ 2 ➤ 1

Each arrow is equivalent to one half value thickness. Thus to reduce to 1 mSv hr^{-1}, eight half value thicknesses are needed.

Total thickness = 8 x 30 = **240 mm** (or 0.24 m) of lead

❑ Shielding can be used to reduce the exposure to radiation, but since gamma rays are electromagnetic radiation they obey the inverse square law:

$$D \propto \frac{1}{r^2} \qquad H \propto \frac{1}{r^2}$$

Thus the exposure can be reduced by increasing the distance from the source.

❑ *Example*
The dose equivalent at 2 m from a gamma source is 20 mSv. How far away must you be to reduce your exposure to 1 mSv?

Step 1 Put the information into symbol form.

H_1 = 20 mSv
H_2 = 1 mSv
r_1 = 2 m

Step 2 Choose the correct equation and complete the equation.

$$H_1 (r_1)^2 = H_2 (r_2)^2$$
$$20 \times 4 = 1 \times r_2^2$$
$$80 = r_2^2$$
$$8.94 \text{ m} = r_2$$

You must be **8.94 m** away to reduce exposure to 1 mSv.

ADDITIONAL CONTENT STATEMENTS

4.1   Units, prefixes and scientific notation

❑   Know the SI units of all physical quantities used in the course (see the list on page 124).

❑   Check all the answers to calculations and give the answers to an appropriate number of significant figures.

❑   Be able to use scientific notation, i.e. numbers like 3×10^8

❑   Know the meaning of and be able to use:

pico (p)	$= 10^{-12}$	kilo (k)	$= 10^3$
nano (n)	$= 10^{-9}$	mega (M)	$= 10^6$
micro (μ)	$= 10^{-6}$	giga (G)	$= 10^9$
milli (m)	$= 10^{-3}$	tera (T)	$= 10^{12}$
centi (c)	$= 10^{-2}$		

4.2   Uncertainties

❑   The measurement of any physical quantity is liable to uncertainty.   The three mains types of uncertainty are:

❑   (1) **Random uncertainties**
Repeated measurements of the same quantity give different readings; uncertainties are as likely to be positive or negative.

❑   (2) **Reading uncertainty**
This is a measure of how well an instrument scale can be read.

❑   (3) **Systematic effects**
These are errors due to faults in the apparatus, e.g. wrong calibration or experimental technique; the error will always be either positive or negative; all the results will be affected the same way.

❑   Repeated measurements of a physical quantity will help to eliminate random uncertainties.

❑   The mean (or average) of a number of measurements of a physical quantity is found by adding up all the measurements and dividing by the number of measurements taken.

❑   This mean value is the best estimate of the "true" value of the quantity being measured.

❏ If there is a systematic error, the mean value will always be too high or too low, i.e. the mean value will be offset from the true value of the physical quantity being measured. For example, if the zero on a thermometer is marked at 5 °C, all temperatures measured using the thermometer will be 5 °C too high.

❏ The approximate random error or uncertainty in the mean value can be found from:

$$\text{random error} = \frac{\text{maximum value - minimum value}}{\text{number of measurements}}$$

❏ For an analogue meter, if the scale division is large the reading uncertainty is taken as half the smallest scale division, e.g. a Bourdon gauge.
Otherwise take the reading uncertainty as equal to the smallest scale division, e.g. for a ruler or a thermometer.

❏ The reading uncertainty for a digital meter is taken as the smallest scale reading,
e.g. for an ammeter reading to 5.99 A, the smallest scale reading is 0.01 A.

❏ Uncertainties can be expressed in **absolute terms**,
e.g. 0.5 ± 0.001 m for a ruler measuring 50 cm;
the absolute error in this measurement is ± 0.001 m.

They can also be expressed in **percentage** terms,
e.g. the percentage uncertainty for the ruler :

$$\% \text{ uncertainty} = \frac{\text{size of absolute uncertainty}}{\text{size of measurement}} \times 100 \%$$

$$= \frac{0.001}{0.5} \times 100 = 0.2 \%$$

length of ruler = 0.5 m ± 0.001 m
or   = 0.5 m ± 0.2 %

❏ In an experiment where more than one physical quantity has been measured, the percentage uncertainty for each can be calculated. Then the quantity with the largest percentage uncertainty can be identified.

❏ The largest percentage uncertainty, for the various quantities measured, is often a good estimate of the percentage uncertainty in the final numerical result of the experiment.

❏ The numerical result of an experiment can be expressed in the form "final value ± absolute uncertainty".

QUANTITIES AND UNITS

	Quantity	Symbol	Unit (SI unit first)
❏	length	l	**m**, mm, cm, km
❏	area	A	m^2, cm^2, mm^2
❏	volume	V	m^3, cm^3, m
❏	distance	d	**m**, cm, km
❏	displacement	s	**m**, cm, km
❏	mass	m	**kg**, g
❏	weight	W	N
❏	time	t	**s**, m, hr
❏	half life	τ	**s**, m, hr, yr
❏	velocity	v	**m s^{-1}**
❏	acceleration	a	**m s^{-2}**
❏	gravitational field strength	g	**N kg^{-1}**
❏	frequency	f	**Hz** (hertz), kHz
❏	wavelength	λ	**m**, cm
❏	period	T	s
❏	energy	E	**J** (joule)
❏	work	E_w	J
❏	force	F	**N** (newton)
❏	power	P	**W** (watt)
❏	momentum		**kg m s^{-1}**
❏	impulse		**N s, kg m s^{-1}**
❏	power of lens	P	**D** (dioptre)
❏	current	I	**A** (ampere)
❏	voltage (p.d.)	V	**V** (volt)
❏	resistance	R	**Ω** (ohm)
❏	charge	Q	**C** (coulomb) , μC
❏	capacitance	C	**F** (farad), μF, pF
❏	temperature	T	**°C, K** (kelvin)
❏	specific heat capacity	c	**J kg^{-1} °C^{-1}, J kg^{-1} K^{-1}**
❏	specific latent heat	L	**J kg^{-1}**
❏	activity	A	**Bq** (bequerel)
❏	absorbed dose	D	**Gy** (gray)
❏	dose equivalent	H	**Sv** (sievert)
❏	density	ρ	**kg m^{-3}**
❏	pressure	P	**Pa** (pascal), N m^{-2}
❏	electric field strength	E	**N C^{-1}**
❏	intensity of illumination	I	**W m^{-2}**

Other symbols

❏	acc. due to gravity	g	9.8 m s^{-2}
❏	quality factor	Q	-
❏	absolute refractive index of a medium	n	-
❏	Plank's constant	h	$(6.64 \times 10^{-34}$ J s$)$

KINEMATICS

☐   Average speed $=\dfrac{\text{total distance}}{\text{total time}}$

☐   Average velocity $=\dfrac{\text{displacement}}{\text{total time}}$

☐ $\bar{v} = \dfrac{d}{t}$ (only for constant or average speed)

☐   Distance = area under speed - time graph

☐   A vector quantity has magnitude (size) and direction, e.g. displacement, velocity, acceleration, force, weight momentum.

☐   A scalar quantity has magnitude only, e.g. distance, speed, energy, power, time.

☐   Vectors must be added 'nose to tail' either by a scale diagram or, if vectors are at right angles, by Pythagoras'. When the result is quoted it **must** include a direction.

☐   Any vector can be resolved into components at right angles:

The four equations of motion are:

☐ $v = u + at$ where s = displacement

☐ $s = ut + \frac{1}{2}at^2$ u = initial velocity

                                       v = final velocity

☐ $s = \dfrac{(u + v)}{2}t$ a = acceleration

                                         t = time

☐ $v^2 = u^2 + 2as$

These equations are only true for constant acceleration.

☐   Note that the term $\dfrac{(u + v)}{2} = \bar{v}$

where $\bar{v}$ = average speed.

☐   **Light gate**
instantaneous velocity $= v = \dfrac{\text{length of card}}{\text{time to cut beam}}$

DYNAMICS

❑ The newton is the net force required to give a mass of 1 kg an acceleration of 1 m s^{-2}.

❑ **Newton's First Law**
A body remains at rest or continues at a constant velocity unless acted upon by an unbalanced force.

❑ **Newton's Second Law**
$F = m\,a$ where F is the unbalanced force in the direction of the motion.

❑ **Newton's Third Law**
If **A** exerts a force on **B**, **B** exerts an equal force on **A** in the opposite direction.

❑ $W = m\,g$

❑ $E_w = F\,d$

❑ $E_p = m\,g\,h$

❑ $E_k = \frac{1}{2}\,m\,v^2$

❑ $v = \sqrt{2\,g\,h}$ since $E_k = E_p$
(Do not use if energy is 'lost' due to friction.)

❑ Energy conservation: if there is apparent energy loss it is usually due to work done against friction:
$F\,d = \text{lost energy}$ where F is the frictional force
d is the displacement

❑ $P = \dfrac{E}{t}$ ($P = F\,v$ for **constant speed**)

❑ **momentum** $= m\,v$

❑ Momentum is conserved in explosions and collisions, provided no external forces act.

❑ In explosions the initial momentum is zero; therefore the total momentum after the explosion is zero.

❑ Elastic collision - momentum and kinetic energy are conserved

❑ Inelastic collision - only momentum is conserved

❑ **impulse** $= F\,t = m\,v - m\,u$

❑ Area under force-time graph $= m\,v - m\,u$

PROPERTIES OF MATTER

❑ $E_h = c\,m\,\Delta T$

❑ $E_h = m\,L$

❑ $L_{\text{vaporisation}}$ - if boiling or condensing

❑ L_{fusion} - if melting or freezing

❑   efficiency $= \dfrac{E_{\text{out}}}{E_{\text{in}}}$ x $100\,\%$ or $\dfrac{P_{\text{out}}}{P_{\text{in}}}$ x $100\,\%$

❑ $P = \dfrac{F}{A}$

❑ $1\,m^2 = 1 \times 10^4\,cm^2 = 1 \times 10^6\,mm^2$

❑ $1\,m^3 = 1 \times 10^6\,cm^3 = 1 \times 10^9\,mm^3$

❑ $\dfrac{P}{T}$ = constant   **Pressure - temperature Law**
     T = temperature in **kelvin**

❑ $0\,K = -273\,^{\circ}C$

❑ $\dfrac{V}{T}$ = constant   **Charles' Law**
     T = temperature in **kelvin**

❑ $P\,V$ = constant   **Boyle's Law**

❑ $\dfrac{P\,V}{T}$ = constant   **General Gas Equation**
     T = temperature in **kelvin**

❑ $\rho = \dfrac{m}{V}$

❑   **pressure in a liquid = density** x g x **depth** $(\rho\,\boldsymbol{g}\,\boldsymbol{h})$

❑   Therefore $P \propto h$ and $P \propto \rho$

❑   Spacing of particles:
     solid - $\boldsymbol{d}$, liquid - $\boldsymbol{d}$, gas - **10$\boldsymbol{d}$** (approx)

❑   Volume change:
     solid - $\boldsymbol{d}^3$, liquid - $\boldsymbol{d}^3$, gas - **1000$\boldsymbol{d}^3$** (approx)

○   **upthrust = weight of liquid displaced**

RESISTORS IN CIRCUITS

❑ $Q = I t$

❑ $V = I R$

❑ $P = I V = I^2 R = \dfrac{V^2}{R}$

❑ $E = I t V = I^2 R t = \dfrac{V^2}{R} t$

❑ $R_T = R_1 + R_2 + R_3 + ...$ resistors in series

❑ $\dfrac{1}{R_T} = \dfrac{1}{R_1} + \dfrac{1}{R_2} + \dfrac{1}{R_3} + ...$ resistors in parallel

❑ $\dfrac{V_s}{V_p} = \dfrac{N_s}{N_p} = \dfrac{I_p}{I_s}$ Transformer equation for
100 % efficiency:
s indicates secondary,
p indicates primary circuit

❑ $E_w = Q V$

❑ Definition of a volt - if it takes one joule of energy to transfer one coulomb of charge between two points then the potential difference between the points is one volt.

❑ If one coulomb of charge passes through a 12 V battery, it gains 12 J of energy.

❑ An electrical source can be thought of as a source of e.m.f., **E** , in series with an internal resistance **r**. **R** is the external load resistor and **I** the current.

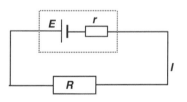

❑ $E = I R + I r$

(e.m.f. = t.p.d. + lost volts)

□   Wheatstone bridge

$$\frac{R_1}{R_2} = \frac{R_3}{R_4}$$ see page 46

○   *Metre bridge*

$$\frac{R_1}{R_2} = \frac{L_1}{100 - L_1}$$ *see page 47*

□   Out of balance Wheatstone bridge

   see page 50

ALTERNATING CURRENT AND VOLTAGE

□   A.C. Theory

$$V_{\text{peak}} = \sqrt{2}\, V_{\text{r.m.s.}} \qquad I_{\text{peak}} = \sqrt{2}\, I_{\text{r.m.s.}}$$

$$V_{\text{r.m.s.}} = \frac{1}{\sqrt{2}}\, V_{\text{peak}} \qquad I_{\text{r.m.s.}} = \frac{1}{\sqrt{2}}\, I_{\text{peak}}$$

□   voltage gain $= \dfrac{\text{voltage out}}{\text{voltage in}}$

□   power gain $= \dfrac{\text{power out}}{\text{power in}}$

CAPACITANCE

❑ $C = \dfrac{Q}{V}$

❑   Energy stored in capacitor:

$$E = \tfrac{1}{2} Q V \;=\; \tfrac{1}{2} C V^2 \;=\; \tfrac{1}{2} \dfrac{Q^2}{C}$$

Charge - discharge characteristics for a capacitor:

❑

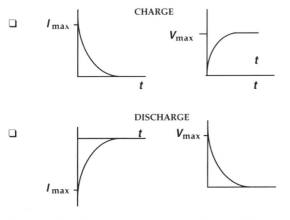

❑   where I_{max} = $V_{max} = V_{supply}$

ANALOGUE ELECTRONICS

❑   In an operational amplifier the inverting mode gain is:

$$\dfrac{V_{supply}}{R}$$
see page 63

❑   In differential mode the gain is:

$$\dfrac{V_o}{V_1} = \dfrac{-R_f}{R_1}$$
see page 68

❑   These gains only apply as long as the calculated value of V_o is less than 85% of the supply voltage to

$$V_o = (V_2 - V_1)\dfrac{R_f}{R_1}$$

the amplifier. If the predicted value is greater than this, then the amplifier is saturated and V_o will equal 85% of supply voltage.

WAVES AND LIGHT

☐ $v = f\,\lambda$

☐ $f = \dfrac{1}{T}$ or $T = \dfrac{1}{f}$

☐   Points in a wave separated by a whole wavelength are in phase.

☐   Points in a wave separated by a half wavelength are out of phase.

☐   Constructive interference - two waves meet in phase.

☐   Destructive interference - two waves meet out of phase.

☐   **path difference** $= n\,\lambda$ for maxima (constructive interference)

☐   **path difference** $= \dfrac{1}{2}\,\lambda,\ 1\dfrac{1}{2}\,\lambda,\ 2\dfrac{1}{2}\,\lambda,\ ......$
                 for minima (destructive interference)

☐   Four characteristic behaviours of waves - reflection, refraction, diffraction and interference.

☐   **Interference** is the test for wave motion.

☐ $d \sin\theta = n\,\lambda$ where **n** is an integer

☐   Wavelengths of light are approximately:

red	-	700 nm
green	-	540 nm
blue	-	490 nm

☐ $n = \dfrac{\sin\theta_1}{\sin\theta_2} = \dfrac{v_1}{v_2} = \dfrac{\lambda_1}{\lambda_2}$

☐ $\sin\theta_c = \dfrac{1}{n}$

☐ $n = \dfrac{1}{\sin\theta_c}$

☐   For all angles of incidence greater than the critical angle, **total internal reflection** takes place.

OPTOELECTRONICS AND SEMICONDUCTORS

SPECTRA

☐   (a) **Prism** - one spectrum, produced by refraction, red deviates least

☐   (b) **Diffraction grating** - pairs of spectra either side of central white maximum, produced by diffraction, red deviates most

☐ $\text{power of lens} = \dfrac{1}{\text{focal length in metres}}$

☐ $I = \dfrac{P}{A}$

☐ $I_1 d_1{}^2 = I_2 d_2{}^2$

☐   Photoelectric emission occurs only if the frequency of the incident radiation is above the threshold frequency, f_o.

☐ $E = h f$

☐ $I = N h f$ where N is the number of photons per second

☐ $E_k = h f - h f_o$
where E_k is the maximum kinetic energy of the photoelectron,
      $h f$ is the energy of the incident photon,
      $h f_o$ is the work function

☐   Emission lines occur when an electron moves from an excited energy level W_2 to a lower energy level W_1 :
$W_2 - W_1 = h f$

☐   An absorption line occurs when an electron in energy level W_1 absorbs radiation of energy $h f$ and moves to excited energy level W_2 :
$W_2 = W_1 + h f$

☐   In semiconductors, **p**-type have **positive** majority charge carriers called holes, which are provided by impurities with one less electron in the outer shell.

☐   n-type have **negative** majority charge carriers called electrons, which are provided by impurities with one more electron in the outer shell.

☐   **p-n** junction:
forward bias (**p**-type to **positive** of supply): conducts
reverse bias (**p**-type to **negative** of supply): does not conduct

NUCLEAR REACTIONS

❏ **Alpha emission** - loss of a helium nucleus (mass number goes down by 4 and atomic number goes down by 2)

❏ **Beta emission** - loss of a high energy electron from the nucleus as a result of a neutron changing into an electron and a proton (mass number unchanged but atomic number goes up by 1)

❏ **Gamma emission** - loss of energy in the form of electromagnetic radiation (no change to either mass number or atomic number)

❏ $A = \dfrac{N}{t}$ where N is the number of atomic nuclei decaying

❏ $D = \dfrac{E}{m}$

❏ $H = D\,Q$

❏ $E = m\,c^2$ c is velocity of light (3×10^8 m s^{-1})

REQUIRED DERIVATIONS

❏ $v = u + a\,t$ see page 11

❏ $s = u\,t + \dfrac{1}{2}a\,t^2$ see page 11

❏ $v^2 = u^2 + 2\,a\,s$ see page 11

❏ $R_T = R_1 + R_2 + R_3 + \dots$ see page 50

❏ $\dfrac{1}{R_T} = \dfrac{1}{R_1} + \dfrac{1}{R_2} + \dfrac{1}{R_3} + \dots$ see page 50

❏ $\sin \theta_c = \dfrac{1}{n}$ see page 90